# TABLE OF CONTENTS

## CREATION OF THE TITANS AND GODS

## THE TWELVE LABORS OF HERACLES

## PROMETHEUS

## CIRCE AND ODYSSEUS

*continued*

TEACHER RESOURCES FOR

# RETOLD
# CLASSIC
# MYTHS

## VOLUME 1

■

Reproducibles
and
Teacher Guide

Editor in Chief: M. Kathleen Myers
Editor: Rebecca Spears Schwartz
Book Designers: Dea Marks
              Deborah Bell
Cover Illustration: Mike Aspengren

CONTRIBUTING
WRITERS

**Randall Jedele**
M.A. English
Educational Writer

**Linda Klatt**
M.S. Education
Language Arts and
  Reading Teacher

**Judith Lawson**
Ph.D. English
Educational Writer

**Sally Master**
M.A. English
Educational Writer

Copyright 1990. Perfection Learning Corporation, Logan, Iowa.

PB ISBN-10: 0-8959-8993-x  ISBN-13: 978-0-8959-8993-2
15 16 17 18 19 20 PP 13 12 11 10 09 08

# Welcome to the Retold Classics ■

## Overview of the Series

The *Retold Classics* literature series includes the following components.

### Six anthologies:

*Retold American Classics, Volume 1*
*Retold American Classics, Volume 2*
*Retold British Classics*
*Retold World Classics*
*Retold Classic Myths, Volume 1*
*Retold Classic Myths, Volume 2*

### Six teacher resource books:

*Retold American Classics, Volume 1*
*Retold American Classics, Volume 2*
*Retold British Classics*
*Retold World Classics*
*Retold Classic Myths, Volume 1*
*Retold Classic Myths, Volume 2*

Each anthology contains eight selections. Each teacher resource book supplies teacher guidelines and reproducible activity sheets for every selection in the companion anthology.

### Reading Levels

#### The Anthologies

The *Retold Classics* are designed for use with students in grades 7-12 who are reading at or above the sixth-grade reading level. The changes made in the selections to accommodate these students are as follows:
- carefully simplified vocabulary
- long sentences divided into manageable units
- challenging words defined
- allusions and references explained in footnotes.

#### The Resource Books

The resource books which accompany the anthologies supply many reproducible activity sheets. The reproducible format allows teachers the freedom to use entire sets of activities or to select individual exercises.

The activities are designed for students reading at or above the sixth-grade level. Lessons build on students' background and experience, providing links between the reader and the text which enhance comprehension and enjoyment.

## Adapting the Classics:
## A Rationale

The *Retold Classics* are based on the premise that all students deserve access to classic literature and that all students are capable of thinking at higher levels if their activities are managed properly.

The *Retold Classics* introduce students who are reading below grade level to stories that are often the exclusive domain of the advanced and college bound. Since the stories are unabridged, students can become familiar with elements of literature through these selections.

### Close Approximation to Originals

Field tests show that the *Retold Classics* are much easier for students to comprehend than the original versions. Yet students experience a close approximation to the author's style and themes in the *Retold* pieces.

Students who read the *Retold Classics* and complete the accompanying activities earn a share in the body of knowledge which defines the culturally literate. They are given the opportunity to understand allusions to great literature and will recognize references to familiar characters and plots. Most important, they will be guided to examine the best in themes and ideals recorded by human beings through the ages.

### Retold Classics Teacher Resource Book:
### Designed for Effective Teaching

The activities in this resource book are arranged in a logical progression, incorporating Madeline Hunter's seven steps of effective teaching and Benjamin Bloom's cognitive taxonomy.

Uniform sets of prereading and postreading activities are compiled for each of the eight selections in *Retold Classic Myths*. Each set contains these elements:

#### Teacher Pages

In each set, the **Teacher Pages** appear first. These pages provide themes for each selection as well as an examination of each activity including the objective, skill levels, description, and suggestions for teaching or adaptation.

#### Prereading Activities

The runway is kept short here. Sometimes students lose interest if the approach is too long. Two brief, but effective activities will get students ready to read. They are as follows:

**Spotlight on Vocabulary**. This prereading activity highlights ten vocabulary words from the **Vocabulary Preview** accompanying each selection in the anthology. (These words also appear in **boldface type** in each work.) Students choose the appropriate word to complete each sentence. The words are used in context similar to that used in the story.

**Setting the Stage**. This second prereading activity provides the anticipatory set for reading the selection. Background and motivation are given in a short, stimulating activity designed to make students more attentive readers.

## Postreading Activities

A rich array of postreading activities is offered. These activities will test recall and comprehension, enhance critical thinking skills, stimulate the imagination, and expose students to important literary skills. Postreading activities include the following:

**It Happened Like This**. The first postreading activity checks understanding of plot development. Recall of important facts and details is tested in a multiple-choice format.

**Vocabulary Review**. Students check their comprehension of the ten words featured in **Spotlight on Vocabulary**. This time, words appear in sentences from the selection. The guided repetition of these words helps build certainty.

**Literary Focus**. The activity zeroes in on developing literary skills by examining plot, character, setting, and themes in a variety of imaginative ways.

**The Reading-Writing Connection: Unlocking Passages**. This postreading activity calls on students first to write their interpretation of a passage from the work and then to make written inferences about it. To conclude the activity, students respond in personal journals to the passage.

**Writing Corner**. This activity is tailored to the selection it addresses. Students might be asked to invent new endings, further round out characters, express a point of view, write a letter, create a humorous tale, write persuasively, or engage in any other writing activity that would be meaningful to the selection at hand. This exercise is carefully designed to take students through prewriting steps that will help them organize their thoughts and ensure that they have something to write about.

**One Step Further**. This section contains a number of suggestions for further extending work with the selection. Class discussion questions, report topics, creative activities, and small-group activities are included here.

## Response Key

Answers to activities are given in the response key.

# CREATION OF THE TITANS AND GODS

## PREREADING ACTIVITIES

### Story Themes

Several themes of "Creation of the Titans and Gods" are listed below. They will help you prepare activities which will stimulate students' interest and involvement in the story.

1.) "Absolute power corrupts absolutely."
2.) Wisdom and compassion are a truer measure of strength than is power.
3.) Even the most powerful are fearful because they have the most to lose.
4.) Tyrants bring about their own downfall.
5.) Eventually a person must face the consequences of his or her actions.

### Spotlight on Vocabulary
### [Guided Practice]

*Objective:*

The learner will demonstrate an understanding of ten vocabulary words by showing which word belongs in each of ten sentences.

*Skill level:*

Knowledge/recall; application

*Description:*

This exercise introduces students to ten words in the story which may be new to them. First students preview the words and their definitions. Then they use the words to complete ten sentences.

The sentences discuss topics familiar to most students, so they can see how the new words fit into their existing web of knowledge. The goal of the exercise is to help students read the story more easily. Complete mastery of the vocabulary words at this stage is not expected.

*Suggestion:*

If prereading vocabulary work is kept short, word study can build interest without dampening enthusiasm. Ex-

posure to these ten selected words will give students a head start toward understanding the story. A *postreading* vocabulary check and suggestions for further vocabulary study are provided for use *after* students have read the story.

### Setting the Stage
### [Anticipatory Set]

*Objective:*

The learner will demonstrate an understanding of *personification* by assigning human traits to natural phenomena. The learner will then demonstrate an understanding of the effects of power on a person's character by listing positive and negative changes which may result from acquiring power.

*Skill level:*

Comprehension; application; analysis

*Description:*

First students are asked to assign human traits to the earth and sky by describing the physical appearance and actions of *Mother Earth* and *Father Sky*. Then students list changes that may occur in a person's character if he or she suddenly became very powerful. These changes are evaluated as positive or negative, with students listing the changes under the appropriate heading.

*continued*

## CREATION OF THE TITANS AND GODS

*Suggestion:*

If your students have short attention spans, you might consider asking them to answer only one of the two sets of questions provided in **Setting the Stage**. Plan to discuss the answers to the questions just before you ask students to read the story. Do not expect to resolve all of the issues that come up. Instead use the momentum generated by the discussion to propel students into the story. You might also help students understand that opinions may differ about whether a specific change in personality is positive or negative.

# CREATION OF THE TITANS AND GODS

## POSTREADING ACTIVITIES

### It Happened Like This
### [Check for Understanding]

*Objective:*

The learner will demonstrate comprehension of the story by correctly answering ten multiple-choice questions.

*Skill level:*

Knowledge; comprehension

*Description:*

This exercise tests recall of important facts in the story. Students identify, from three choices, the answer that correctly completes each of ten sentences.

*Suggestion:*

Page number references on the response key show where the answer to each question can be found. These page numbers can be given to students who are taking an open-book test. The page numbers are also helpful when discussing the quiz after papers have been corrected.

### Vocabulary Review
### [Check for Understanding]

*Objective:*

The learner will demonstrate an understanding of ten words by identifying the correct synonym for each.

*Skill level:*

Knowledge

*Description:*

This exercise tests mastery of the ten words introduced in the **Spotlight on Vocabulary** exercise. The words are presented in the context of sentences taken directly from the story. Students identify, from three choices, the correct synonym for each word.

*Suggestion:*

Results of the vocabulary check will show which words students find most difficult. You may wish to provide further reinforcement of problem words.

### Literary Focus: The Clash of the Titans
### [Guided or Independent Practice]

*Objective:*

The learner will demonstrate an understanding of *conflict* by identifying opposing forces in scenes from the story and determining what type of conflict occurs.

*Skill level:*

Analysis; evaluation

*Description:*

Students are given a list of five major types of conflict. Then they are asked to analyze story passages to determine the opposing forces and type of conflict present.

*Suggestion:*

Before tackling this exercise, students may find it helpful to discuss the forces and types of conflict in terms of their own lives. Have them identify forces which may cause conflict for them.

### The Reading-Writing Connection:
### Unlocking Passages
### [Guided or Independent Practice]

*Objective:*

The learner will demonstrate an ability to make inferences by answering questions based on quotations from the story.

*Skill level:*

Comprehension; application; analysis

*Description:*

First students read a quotation; then they answer three questions about the quote. The first question requires an interpretation of the quote. The second question requires an inference. The third question, to be answered in a journal entry, asks students to relate the quotation to their personal experience.

*continued*

# CREATION OF THE TITANS AND GODS

The questions are intended to lead students to greater understanding and appreciation of the story. The questions also allow students to bridge the gap between their own knowledge and story concepts.

Quotation 1 concerns Gaea's decision to finally seek revenge against Uranus. Quotation 2 concerns Uranus' pain at the realization that he has been defeated. Quotation 3 concerns Zeus' understanding that he must share his power in order to keep it.

*Suggestion:*

Make the questions the subject of a small-group or class discussion.

## Writing Corner: The Ways of Nature
### [Extending Students' Thinking]

*Objective:*

The learner will demonstrate an understanding of the use of myths to explain events in nature by writing a myth-like story about a natural event.

*Skill level:*

Application; analysis; synthesis

*Description:*

Students will choose a natural event to write about from a list and invent a fantasy character who will appear in their story as well. Next they will choose a general story line and outline their story. Then each student will write a draft of the story, let a classmate review it, and finally, revise and share the story.

*Suggestion:*

Students may choose to share their stories either by reading them orally or by publishing them in a classroom anthology.

## One Step Further
### [Extending Students' Thinking]

*Objective:*

The learner will demonstrate an ability to interpret, compare, contrast, and/or create by participating in discussions, preparing reports, or completing special projects.

*Skill level:*

Application; analysis; synthesis; evaluation

*Description:*

Students choose from an array of suggested follow-up activities which will help them process the story and respond creatively to the story's conflicts and themes. The activities encourage students of varying abilities to employ higher-level thinking skills.

*Suggestion:*

You may wish to use this page as a teacher reference and assign projects to individuals or groups. However the page may also be reproduced so that students can select their own topics.

Although the suggested activities are divided into categories such as **Class discussion** and **Written or oral reports**, most of the topics can be adapted for use in many ways.

Name _____

## SPOTLIGHT ON VOCABULARY

Study the words and meanings shown in the box.
Then complete each sentence below by writing the
correct word on the line.

| | |
|---|---|
| **agile**—quick; nimble | **reign**—period of rule |
| **counsel**—advice | **sickle**—cutting tool with a |
| **immortal**—living forever; deathless | curved blade |
| **inevitable**—certain to happen; | **sprouted**—grew |
| unavoidable | **thwarted**—stopped; prevented |
| **infinite**—having no limits; endless | **vial**—small bottle |

1. The cruel king's _____ ended when the people rebelled
   against him.

2. It was _____ that the two ships would run into each
   other unless one of them changed course.

3. Mina planned to go to college, but her plans were
   _____ because she couldn't get the money to go.

4. Henry carried (a, an) _____ containing medicine in case
   he had an allergy attack.

5. Lucia planted flower seeds and then waited for several weeks until the tiny
   plants finally _____ .

6. (A, An) _____ being, such as a god, will never die.

7. The farmer cut the overgrown weeds with (a, an) _____ .

8. There may be no boundaries to outer space; it may be
   _____ .

9. Joshua followed his lawyer's directions and _____ when
   he refused to sign the contract.

10. The _____ boy flipped two times in midair before land-
    ing on his feet.

Name _____

## SETTING THE STAGE

These questions will help you get ready to read "Creation of the Titans and Gods." Prepare to discuss the questions by jotting down answers on the lines.

1.  This myth tells the ancient Greeks' view of creation. In the myth, the earth (Gaea) and the sky (Uranus) are the first parents. They have human traits, and they act like humans.

    Suppose you were asked to *personify* (or give human traits to) the earth and sky. What traits would you give them? Write a description of each character below.

    a. Mother Earth would look like this:

    _____

    _____

    _____

    She would act like this:

    _____

    _____

    _____

    b. Father Sky would look like this:

    _____

    _____

    _____

    He would act like this:

    _____

    _____

    _____

    As you read the story, notice what traits Gaea and Uranus have. Are they similar to the traits which you gave the earth and sky or are they different?

*continued*

2. This myth tells about a power struggle among the mightiest gods. It shows what can happen to very humanlike characters who assume powers.

   Make your own list of changes that might result in a person's character if he or she suddenly became very powerful. Also decide if each change is good or bad. List the changes in the appropriate column below.

| **Good Changes** | **Bad Changes** |
| --- | --- |
|  |  |

Name _____

## IT HAPPENED LIKE THIS

Write the letter of the best answer on the line.

_____ 1. Gaea made her son Uranus her equal so he would
a. surround her on all sides.
b. worship her.
c. turn to her for advice.

_____ 2. The children of Gaea and Uranus include all of the following *except* the
a. Hundred-handed Ones.
b. Furies.
c. Cyclopes.

_____ 3. Uranus hurls his sons into Tartarus because he
a. is ashamed of their stupidity.
b. fears they might someday overpower him.
c. discovers that they hate him.

_____ 4. When the Titans are born, Gaea
a. tells them to respect Uranus.
b. warns them to stay away from Uranus.
c. asks them to help conquer Uranus.

_____ 5. Cronus overthrows his father because he wants to
a. become the supreme ruler.
b. help his mother free her children.
c. please his wife.

_____ 6. Gaea warns Cronus that he will be
a. dethroned by one of his own sons.
b. tortured in the Underworld.
c. overthrown by the Cyclopes.

_____ 7. Cronus thinks he has defeated fate when he
a. kills the Cyclopes.
b. marries Rhea.
c. swallows his babies.

_____ 8. Cronus drinks the drink Zeus gives him and then
a. becomes immortal.
b. throws up his children.
c. breathes fire on Zeus.

_____ 9. After Cronus rejects Prometheus' advice, Prometheus
a. flees to Tartarus.
b. threatens to eat Cronus' children.
c. goes to Zeus and advises him.

_____ 10. In the end, Cronus and the Titans
a. are defeated by Zeus.
b. conquer Zeus.
c. share their power with Zeus.

RETOLD CLASSIC MYTHS, VOL. 1

Copyright 1990. Perfection Learning Corporation, Logan, Iowa 51546

# CREATION OF THE TITANS AND GODS

## VOCABULARY REVIEW

These sentences are taken from the story. Circle the answer that comes closest in meaning to each word in **dark type**.

1. "Just small bits of things floated through **infinite** space."
   a. darkest     b. endless     c. chilly

2. "They swirled faster and faster until the first **immortal** being, Eros—or Love—appeared."
   a. deathless     b. smart     c. beautiful

3. "Each of these giants **sprouted** fifty heads from his mighty shoulders."
   a. cut     b. nodded     c. grew

4. "So [Gaea] took a piece of stone and shaped it into a sharp **sickle**."
   a. pitchfork     b. fountain pen     c. cutting tool

5. "And at the moment, knowing his **reign** was over pained [Uranus] more deeply than his wounds."
   a. marriage     b. rule     c. sleep

6. "She wanted children so much. Yet it was **inevitable** that her cruel husband would destroy every one."
   a. certain     b. possible     c. foolish

7. " 'There!' [Cronus] thought once again. 'The child is gone. I have **thwarted** fate again.' "
   a. confused     b. stopped     c. predicted

8. "[Zeus] learned grace as well from dancing with the **agile** nymphs."
   a. nimble     b. happy     c. agreeable

9. "Then [Gaea] handed him a small **vial**. 'When your father is thirsty, give this to him to swallow.' "
   a. bottle     b. fruit     c. wine glass

10. "Prometheus realized Cronus was too stupid to accept the wise **counsel**."
    a. wizard     b. story     c. advice

# CREATION OF THE TITANS AND GODS

## LITERARY FOCUS: THE CLASH OF THE TITANS

"Creation of the Titans and Gods" focuses on several types of *conflict*. These conflicts create tension. They also make the reader want to finish the story to see how the conflicts end. The five major types of conflict are listed below.

---

a. **Character vs. self:** a character struggles against his or her own emotions or thoughts. For example, a character may both love and hate someone.

b. **Character vs. nature:** a character struggles against forces of nature such as storms or rugged country.

c. **Character vs. society:** a character struggles against forces of society such as laws or social codes.

d. **Character vs. others:** a character struggles against another person, humanlike character, or group.

e. **Character vs. fate:** a character struggles against accidents, coincidences, prophecies, or god(s).

---

The following passages are taken from the myth. For each scene, write the two opposing forces. Then write the letter of the appropriate conflict from the list above.

Note that some scenes may contain more than one type of conflict. But you need to name only one type. Also, not all types are used. The first problem is done for you.

1. "Uranus looked upon his offspring with horror. He knew that their strength would be far greater than his own.

   Uranus took care of his threat in a brutal way. After each son was born, Uranus hurled him deep into the earth." (pages 4-5)

   **The opposing forces**   *Uranus vs. his offspring*

   **Type of conflict**   *d*

*continued*

2. "Gaea . . . was shocked by her husband's actions. She deeply grieved for her children. Yet she kept her feelings quiet, for she knew revenge would be hers one day." (page 5)

   **The opposing forces** _____

   **Type of conflict** _____

3. "A soft chuckle came from behind Gaea's sons. It came from the youngest son, Cronus. He was laughing at his cowardly brothers.

   'Not one of you has the courage to help Mother? I'm surprised at you,' Cronus said with a mocking smile." (page 6)

   **The opposing forces** _____

   **Type of conflict** _____

4. "At first, it seemed that Cronus would indeed triumph. But in time, fate began to work on him. He fell in love with and married his sister, Rhea." (page 7)

   **The opposing forces** _____

   **Type of conflict** _____

5. "Cronus gazed at little Hestia with adoring eyes. Suddenly Gaea's words screamed in his head. Cronus' eyes became boiling pools of madness. He grabbed the baby from Rhea's arms and quickly swallowed her." (page 7)

   **The opposing forces** _____

   **Type of conflict** _____

6. "[Cronus] seized the bundle, opened his huge mouth, and swallowed it. Then he smacked his lips happily.

   'There!' he thought once again. 'The child is gone. I have thwarted fate again. No one is cleverer than I am!' " (page 8)

   **The opposing forces** _____

   **Type of conflict** _____

*continued*

7. "Cronus bellowed, 'Son or no son! No one will take my throne! He'll have to fight me and all the other Titans!'
   Zeus accepted the challenge." (page 10)

**The opposing forces** _____

**Type of conflict** _____

8. "The Hundred-handed Ones broke off huge boulders from cliffs. Then they pelted the Titans, causing the whole earth to shake. . . .
   From the heavens, Zeus flung bolts of thunder and lightning at Cronus. The fiery bolts caused the forests to catch fire. The seas boiled and bubbled, too. Even the sky hissed with flames and seemed ready to crash to the ground." (page 11)

**The opposing forces** _____

**Type of conflict** _____

RETOLD CLASSIC MYTHS, VOL. 1
Copyright 1990. Perfection Learning Corporation, Logan, Iowa 51546

Name _____

## THE READING-WRITING CONNECTION: UNLOCKING PASSAGES

Answer the questions about these quotes taken from "Creation of the Titans and Gods." (Go back to the story if you need more clues.) Write your response to part *c* of each question on a separate sheet of paper.

1. "With the birth of the Titans, Gaea realized the time had come to take revenge against Uranus." (page 5)

   a. What does the passage mean as used in the story?

   _____

   _____

   b. Why do you think Gaea waited until the Titans were born to get revenge? Was her revenge justified? Explain.

   _____

   _____

   _____

   _____

   c. **Journal writing:** Describe a time when you wanted revenge. If you took revenge, did the situation get better or worse? If you decided against revenge, tell why.

2. "Of course, Uranus was immortal and could not die. But he could feel pain. And at the moment, knowing his reign was over pained him more deeply than his wounds." (page 6)

   a. What does the passage mean as used in the story?

   _____

   _____

*continued*

b. Why do you think Uranus felt pain when he realized his reign was over?

_____

_____

_____

_____

c. **Journal writing:** Describe what it would be like to become powerless after having once been powerful.

3.  "Unlike his father and grandfather, Zeus wisely decided to share his power. Though he remained supreme ruler, he allowed others to control parts of his kingdom." (page 11)

a. What does the passage mean as used in the story?

_____

_____

b. For what reasons was Zeus willing to share his power? Do you believe this was a wise decision? Why or why not?

_____

_____

_____

_____

c. **Journal writing:** Tell about a time when you or someone you know shared power (at home, in a club, etc.). What were the benefits of sharing power? What were the drawbacks?

## WRITING CORNER:
## THE WAYS OF NATURE

This myth explains many things that happen in
nature. For instance, the god Helios is said to move
the sun across the sky. Also, the storms are controlled by the Cyclopes, while the heavens are held in
place by Atlas.

Now make up your own story to explain a part of
nature. For instance, your story might tell how earthquakes happen or how waterfalls were born. Include
at least one fantasy character in your story.

1. Read the following list. Then check which natural event you will
   write about.

   ☐ earthquakes      ☐ volcanoes

   ☐ eclipses      ☐ tidal waves

   ☐ tornadoes or hurricanes      ☐ rain or snow

   ☐ seasons      ☐ other (specify)_____

2. Next describe your fantasy character. Be sure to give the character a
   name and tell what part he or she will play in the story.

   _____

   _____

   _____

   _____

   _____

   _____

3. Now check which general storyline you will use.

   ☐ why the natural event first occurred

   ☐ how the natural event occurs

   ☐ other (specify)_____

*continued*

4.  Briefly outline your story below.

_____

_____

_____

_____

_____

_____

_____

5.  Now write your story on a separate sheet of paper. Use your notes
    and outline to help you. When you are finished, let a classmate read
    your story and suggest improvements. Then revise your story and
    share it with others.

## ONE STEP FURTHER

### Class discussion

1. How is Zeus different from his father and grandfather? Why do you think he turns out differently?

2. Compare and contrast the use (or abuse) of power by Uranus, Cronus, and Zeus.

3. How does the old saying "Pride goeth before a fall" apply to this story?

4. What special powers and traits does Gaea have? In what ways does she seem helpless? What do her character traits reveal about the Greeks' view of women?

5. Both Uranus and Cronus are described as supreme rulers. Yet they have weaknesses and are not as strong as other forces in the story. Name their weaknesses and identify the stronger forces. Then explain why the two gods lost power.

6. This myth has been called the story of civilization's birth. Explain how readers could view the myth this way.

### Written or oral reports

1. Compare the Greek story of creation to some modern scientific theories of the universe's birth. Report on the similarities and differences you find in the ancient and modern views.

2. Report on other stories about the creation of the world. Some, such as the Babylonian account (Enuma Elish), the Hindu (Rig Veda), and the Norse (Elder Eddas), can be found in *Myths of Creation and Fall* by Rita Oleyar. Compare and contrast traits of the creator(s) and the process of creation in these accounts.

3. Do some research on Zeus after he became chief of the gods. What evidence is there that he could be unjust, cruel, and foolish? How did he also show himself to be fair, kind, and wise? At the conclusion of your report, rate the god as a leader on a scale of one to ten (ten being high).

### Creative writing activities

1. Write five analogies based upon information found within this story. (For instance, *Gaea : earth :: Uranus : sky*).

2. Design a crossword puzzle based upon the information in this story. Begin with a list of twenty words and a brief definition of each. Then arrange the words into a crossword puzzle, providing the appropriate spaces and clues for each word. Include an answer key on a separate page.

3. Compose an original ballad or folk song retelling the events of this story. You may use a familiar melody or create a new one.

4. Create a comic book based upon this story. Include cartoon balloons with the characters' words as well as narration at the top of the cartoon boxes.

### Artistic activities

1. Create a "family tree" (genealogical chart) showing the characters in this myth. You may wish to color-code your chart to help viewers. For instance, with color-coding you can show whether the character is male or female, monstrous or humanlike, important or unimportant, good or bad. You also may want to include small illustrations to indicate each god's power.

2. Create a filmstrip that illustrates and retells the story for a younger class. Or draw your illustrations on a large flip chart and use these to retell the myth. Be sure to keep in mind the vocabulary and interest level of your audience.

3. Create a game based on this myth. Include the characters, major events, and problems encountered in the story.

*continued*

## Small-group discussion

1. With a group of other students, debate the saying ''Absolute [or total] power corrupts absolutely.'' Find historical evidence to back up your opinion. Then in front of the class, debate a group with opposing views. At the conclusion of the debate, welcome questions and then take a vote on the issue.

2. Do children owe their parent(s) respect and obedience? At what point are children justified in rebelling against their parent(s)? Discuss these questions with a small group. When you have some general guidelines you can agree upon, offer your views to the rest of the class.

## PROMETHEUS

# PREREADING ACTIVITIES

### Story Themes

Several themes of "Prometheus" are listed below. They will help you prepare activities which will stimulate students' interest and involvement in the story.

1.) People tend to care deeply about those for whom they have taken responsibility.
2.) Gifts often come at a price.
3.) It is sometimes necessary to defy authority in order to stand up for what you believe.
4.) Things that are important in our lives require careful attention.
5.) A person who chooses to defy authority must be willing to suffer the consequences.

### Spotlight on Vocabulary
### [Guided Practice]

*Objective:*

The learner will demonstrate an understanding of ten vocabulary words by showing which word belongs in each of ten sentences.

*Skill level:*

Knowledge/recall; application

*Description:*

This exercise introduces students to ten words in the story which may be new to them. First students preview the words and their definitions. Then they use the words to complete ten sentences.

The sentences discuss topics familiar to most students, so they can see how the new words fit into their existing web of knowledge. The goal of the exercise is to help students read the story more easily. Complete mastery of the vocabulary words at this stage is not expected.

*Suggestion:*

If prereading vocabulary work is kept short, word study can build interest without dampening enthusiasm. Exposure to these ten selected words will give students a head start toward understanding the story. A *postreading* vocabulary check and suggestions for further vocabulary study are provided for use *after* students have read the story.

### Setting the Stage
### [Anticipatory Set]

*Objective:*

The learner will demonstrate an understanding of the harshness of life faced by characters in the myth by reacting to a similar, modern-day situation. The learner will also consider Prometheus' traits and predict whether or nor he will prove likeable.

*Skill level:*

Application; analysis; evaluation

*Description:*

In part 1, students imagine that some of their neighbors have lost their jobs and homes. Then they are asked to view the situation from three perspectives: that of a person who doesn't care, one who cares but doesn't do anything, and one who cares and helps.

In part 2, students are given a list of Prometheus' character traits and asked to describe how each trait can be both positive and negative. From their examples, students will predict whether Prometheus will be a likeable character.

*Suggestion:*

Have students discuss the positive and negative side of common character traits.

# POSTREADING ACTIVITIES

## It Happened Like This
### [Check for Understanding]

*Objective:*

The learner will demonstrate comprehension of the story by correctly answering ten multiple-choice questions.

*Skill level:*

Knowledge; comprehension

*Description:*

This exercise tests recall of important facts in the story. Students identify, from three choices, the answer that correctly completes each of ten sentences.

*Suggestion:*

Page number references on the response key show where the answer to each question can be found. These page numbers can be given to students who are taking an open-book test. The page numbers are also helpful when discussing the quiz after papers have been corrected.

## Vocabulary Review
### [Check for Understanding]

*Objective:*

The learner will demonstrate an understanding of ten words by identifying the correct synonym for each.

*Skill level:*

Knowledge

*Description:*

This exercise tests mastery of the ten words introduced in the **Spotlight on Vocabulary** exercise. The words are presented in the context of sentences taken directly from the story. Students identify, from three choices, the correct synonym for each word.

*Suggestion:*

Results of the vocabulary check will show which words students find most difficult. You may wish to provide further reinforcement for problem words.

## Literary Focus: It's Alive!
### [Guided or Independent Practice]

*Objective:*

The learner will demonstrate an understanding of personification by analyzing passages from the myth in which ideas or things take on human qualities.

*Skill level:*

Analysis

*Description:*

Students complete a chart by analyzing passages from the myth which contain examples of personification. For each example they are asked to identify what is personified and which human traits are taken on.

*Suggestion:*

Discuss the use of personification in the myth. Help students realize that personification can help make writing more colorful and interesting. Have them find examples of personification in other myths they have read. Also, students might enjoy writing passages in which common items in the classroom or at home are personified.

## The Reading-Writing Connection:
## Unlocking Passages
### [Guided or Independent Practice]

*Objective:*

The learner will demonstrate an ability to make inferences by answering questions based on quotations from the story.

*Skill level:*

Comprehension; application; analysis

*Description:*

First students read a quotation; then they answer three questions about the quote. The first question requires an inter-

*continued*

pretation of the quote. The second question requires an inference. The third question, to be answered in a journal entry, asks students to relate the quotation to their personal experience.

The questions are intended to lead students to greater understanding and appreciation of the story. The questions also allow students to bridge the gap between their own knowledge and story concepts. Quotation 1 concerns Prometheus' love for the humans he has created and set upon the earth. Quotation 2 concerns Zeus' urge to destroy those who do not give him proper respect. Quotation 3 concerns the unwillingness of Zeus to forgive Prometheus and Zeus' subsequent punishment of the human race.

*Suggestion:*
Make the questions the subject of a small-group or class discussion.

### Writing Corner: Get the Picture
### [Extending Students' Thinking]

*Objective:*
The learner will demonstrate an understanding of the use of imagery in the myth by writing sentences which contain images pertaining to each of the senses.

*Skill level:*
Comprehension; application

*Description:*
First, students imagine that they are one of the humans in the myth who lives in a cave. They are then to write five images—one for each sense—describing life before having fire. Next students write five images describing life after acquiring fire. In a final step, students use their images to write a description of life before and after having fire.

*Suggestion:*
Ask for volunteers to share their descriptive writing and have students identify examples of imagery found in the writing samples.

### One Step Further
### [Extending Students' Thinking]

*Objective:*
The learner will demonstrate an ability to interpret, compare, contrast, and/or create by participating in discussions, preparing reports, or completing special projects.

*Skill level:*
Application; analysis; synthesis; evaluation

*Description:*
Students choose from an array of suggested follow-up activities which will help them process the story and respond creatively to the story's conflicts and themes. The activities encourage students of varying abilities to employ higher-level thinking skills.

*Suggestion:*
You may wish to use this page as a teacher reference and assign projects to individuals or groups. However the page may also be reproduced so that students can select their own topics.

Although the suggested activities are divided into categories such as **Class discussion** and **Written or oral reports**, most of the topics can be adapted for use in many ways.

# PROMETHEUS

## SPOTLIGHT ON VOCABULARY

Study the words and meanings shown in the box.
Then complete each sentence below by writing the
correct word on the line.

> **deceptive**—misleading; false
> **defied**—challenged or disobeyed
> **destined**—certain; predecided
> **hovered**—waited (especially at one
>     place in the air)
> **humility**—modesty; freedom from pride
>
> **provocation**—cause or reason
> **soothed**—calmed; comforted
> **stern**—strict; harsh
> **tactic**—plan; approach
> **tend**—watch over; care for

1. Our new boss is so _____ that she forces
   you to make up an hour of work if you're fifteen minutes late.

2. A _____ T.V. offer led Jon to believe he could
   receive free magazines, but of course he never did.

3. She seems _____ for success because she has common
   sense and works hard.

4. The band members' latest _____ to get new uniforms
   is to ask for donations after every show.

5. The teenagers _____ the curfew by staying out later
   than they should have.

6. The helicopter _____ over the scene of the accident,
   waiting to transport victims.

7. Without _____, the bully picked a fight with a
   terrified classmate.

8. After the meet, Tomas showed _____ by refusing to
   brag about his win in front of the other swimmers.

9. The teacher's calm voice _____ the frightened child.

10. It was Marie's job to _____ the animals and see that
    they were fed and exercised.

Name _____  **PROMETHEUS**

## SETTING THE STAGE

These questions will help you get ready to read
"Prometheus." Prepare to discuss the questions by
jotting down your answers on the lines.

1. In the myth, you will read that humans had a very tough life. Imagine a similar situation in modern life. It is winter. Some people in your neighborhood have lost their jobs and their homes.

   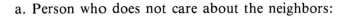

   What opinion would the following people have about their unfortunate neighbors? Write several sentences from the viewpoint of each of these people. Be sure to give reasons for their opinions and actions.

   a. Person who does not care about the neighbors:

   _____

   _____

   _____

   b. Person who cares but does nothing to help:

   _____

   _____

   _____

   c. Person who cares and does help the neighbors:

   _____

   _____

   _____

   Now share your work with other classmates. You might also discuss whether or not people in categories *a* and *b* are ever justified in their opinions and actions.

*continued*

2. Below are some traits of Prometheus, the main character in the myth. As you read the traits, give an example to show how the trait can be positive. Then indicate how the trait can be negative. The first one is done for you.

| POSITIVE SIDE | TRAITS | NEGATIVE SIDE |
|---|---|---|
| *will stick to something and see that it is done* | strong-willed | *may insist on doing something stupid* |
| | rebellious | |
| | daring | |
| | accepts fate | |
| | unremorseful (shows no regret for deeds) | |
| | prefers to be alone | |

Now that you've finished your checklist, weigh the positive and negative traits. Predict whether or not you'll like Prometheus and explain your feelings.

# PROMETHEUS

## IT HAPPENED LIKE THIS

Write the letter of the best answer on the line.

_____ 1. As the story opens, we learn that humans
  a. enjoy being teased by Zeus.
  b. curse Prometheus for creating them.
  c. must endure cold weather and darkness.

_____ 2. Prometheus wants to give fire to humans so they will
  a. be better equipped to survive.
  b. worship him more than they worship Zeus.
  c. set the earth on fire and destroy one another.

_____ 3. Zeus disagrees with Prometheus because he
  a. worries that humans might burn themselves.
  b. thinks there isn't enough fire to share with the whole human race.
  c. believes that fire would give humans power, envy, and greed.

_____ 4. Zeus has refused to provide humans with more comforts since Prometheus
  a. stole from Zeus' water supply to give humans water.
  b. tricked Zeus into taking the poor part of animal sacrifices.
  c. sparked the war between the Titans and Zeus.

_____ 5. Prometheus disobeys Zeus by
  a. throwing water on Zeus' own fire.
  b. taking a burning coal from the gods' central fire.
  c. asking the Sun to give fire to humans.

_____ 6. Prometheus gives fire to the humans and then
  a. tells them they must now worship him for his help.
  b. asks them to hide the gift from Zeus.
  c. shows them how to build, tend, and put out one.

_____ 7. When Zeus discovers what Prometheus has done, he sends Hephaestus to
  a. make a chain that will hold Prometheus to a rock forever.
  b. start an earthquake and destroy life on earth.
  c. take back fire from the human race.

*continued*

____ 8.   Zeus also commands that every
          day through eternity
          a. Prometheus' hands will be
             burned with a torch.
          b. a vulture will tear out
             Prometheus' liver.
          c. Hephaestus will pound
             another spike into
             Prometheus' body.

____ 9.   Prometheus reveals that he has
          a. an important secret.
          b. the power to break free.
          c. one last gift to humans.

____ 10.  Prometheus accepts his fate
          because he
          a. loves Zeus and regrets defying
             him.
          b. believes Zeus is punishing him
             for his own good.
          c. expected to be punished but
             feels pleased that he helped
             humans.

## VOCABULARY REVIEW

These sentences are taken from the story. Circle the
answer that comes closest in meaning to each word in
**dark type**.

1. "Zeus was a great provider, but he was also a **stern** punisher."
   a. careless          b. strict          c. smart

2. "But Prometheus wasn't willing to give up so easily. He stepped in
   front of Zeus and tried another **tactic**."
   a. plan          b. answer          c. plea

3. "Zeus picked the **deceptive** bundle of fat and bones."
   a. misleading          b. huge          c. smelly

4. " 'They need very little **provocation** to become boastful toads.' "
   a. praise          b. time          c. cause

5. " 'If we give them fire. . . . Well, forget about **humility** or devo-
   tion. With fire, they'll think they're gods.' "
   a. humbleness          b. courage          c. happiness

6. " 'Don't be frightened,' Prometheus **soothed** them."
   a. begged          b. comforted          c. asked

7. " 'This fire can change your whole life. But you must learn how to
   **tend** it. You must feed it many twigs or it will die.' "
   a. pray for          b. care for          c. look for

8. "The bird gave a hungry cry as it **hovered** overhead."
   a. soared          b. flapped          c. waited

9. "Thetis' son was **destined** to be greater than his father, no matter
   who his father was."
   a. said          b. certain          c. trying

10. "Yes, he would lie here in pain for years upon years. But he had
    **defied** the gods and given his beloved humans a future."
    a. disobeyed          b. outwitted          c. hurt

# PROMETHEUS

## LITERARY FOCUS: IT'S ALIVE!

In the myth of Prometheus, fire—among other things—comes alive through *personification*.

Personification means giving human qualities to objects, animals, or ideas. Read this example from the myth:

" 'Fire fears water and will fade at its touch.' "

Here, fire takes on a human quality. It feels an emotion—fear.

Study the following passages which contain personification. Then fill in the chart. Tell what is personified. Then write how it is like a human. Give the traits or qualities it has taken on.

| PASSAGE | THING(S) PERSONIFIED | HUMAN QUALITIES OR TRAITS |
|---|---|---|
| 1. " 'Soon one human would have more than the next. Envy and greed would be born.' " (page 19) | | |
| 2. " 'The bed is ready,' Prometheus murmured. 'Now for my sleeping coal.' " (page 21) | | |
| 3. "The flames grew fatter." (page 21) | | |
| 4. "The hungry flames cracked and smacked as the fat oozed down." (page 22) | | |

*continued*

RETOLD CLASSIC MYTHS, VOL. 1

| PASSAGE | THING(S) PERSONIFIED | HUMAN QUALITIES OR TRAITS |
|---|---|---|
| 5. " 'But you must learn how to tend [fire]. You must feed it many twigs or it will die.' " (page 22) | | |
| 6. " 'But don't feed it too much or it will devour everything in sight. Even you!' " (page 22) | | |
| 7. " 'But when the day comes that Zeus gives in, both I and the secret shall be set free.' " (page 24) | | |

Discuss your answers with your classmates. Also, consider what Zeus and Prometheus themselves might personify. Give examples from the myth to support your opinion.

Name _____

## THE READING-WRITING CONNECTION: UNLOCKING PASSAGES

Answer the questions about these quotes taken from "Prometheus." (Go back to the story if you need more clues.) Write your response to part *c* of each question on a separate sheet of paper.

1. "Perhaps Prometheus loved the human race so much because he had created them. From a mix of earth and water, he had molded human shapes in the image of the gods. Then he blew the breath of life into those bodies. Finally he set humankind free to roam the earth." (page 18)

   a. What does this passage mean as used in the story?

   _____

   _____

   b. Do you think Prometheus would have gone to such lengths to provide for humans if they had been created by Zeus?

   _____

   _____

   _____

   _____

   c. **Journal writing:** Describe something or someone you took care of and loved very much.

2. "If humankind didn't pray to Zeus and fear his power, he would destroy them." (page 18)

   a. What does this passage mean as used in the story?

   _____

   _____

*continued*

b. Why do you think it is so important to Zeus that humans worship and fear him?

_____

_____

_____

_____

c. **Journal writing:** Why do some people seem to need praise or worship? Write about someone you know who needs or demands to be treated in this way.

3. "No, Zeus wouldn't soon forget or forgive Prometheus' plan. In fact, since that time Zeus had angrily denied humans most comforts." (page 20)

a. What does this passage mean as used in the story?

_____

_____

b. Suppose Prometheus had not tricked Zeus before. Do you think Zeus would be more willing to give humans fire? Explain.

_____

_____

_____

_____

c. **Journal writing:** Write about a time when you or someone you know found it difficult to forgive someone for playing a trick. Describe what you think makes the forgiving difficult.

## WRITING CORNER: GET THE PICTURE

Descriptions that call up a picture or feeling are called *images*. Images appeal to your sense of sight, sound, touch (feel), taste, or smell.

In "Prometheus," the story becomes more vivid through the use of images. This is because *imagery* gets you involved in the story. It helps you imagine more easily.

Read this image from the myth:

> "After a quick glance around, he reached into the fire and brought out a coal.
>
> 'A jewel fit for my humans,' Prometheus whispered to himself."

In this passage, the image describing fire appeals to your sense of sight. Instead of a mere lump of coal, you can almost see a glimmering, glowing jewel.

Now imagine you are one of the humans living in a cave. Think about what your life would be like *before* having fire. Write five images—one for each sense—that describe your life. Use complete sentences when you write your images.

1. **Sight image:**

   _____

   _____

2. **Smell image:**

   _____

   _____

3. **Sound image:**

   _____

   _____

4. **Taste image:**

   _____

   _____

*continued*

5. **Touch image:**

   _____

   _____

One day Prometheus steals fire from Olympus and gives it to you and other humans. How does your life change? Write five images to describe your life now that you have fire.

1. **Sight image:**

   _____

   _____

2. **Smell image:**

   _____

   _____

3. **Sound image:**

   _____

   _____

4. **Taste image:**

   _____

   _____

5. **Touch image:**

   _____

   _____

Using your images, write a description of life before and after fire is introduced. Try to make your description as colorful and vivid as possible.

# PROMETHEUS

## ONE STEP FURTHER

### Class discussion

1. About fire, Zeus tells Prometheus, " 'Each gift comes at a price. That is fate.' " Later on, Prometheus remembers this when a man burns his tongue. What other price will humans pay for receiving fire? What price does Prometheus pay? In your view, is the price worth it for humans and for Prometheus?

2. Prometheus is famous for his quick wit and trickery. Find examples of his craftiness in the myth. Is this a good quality in Prometheus? Why or why not?

3. Reread the first three paragraphs of the myth. What descriptive words tell about the setting? How do these words help set the mood (overall feeling) of the story?

4. Zeus claims that one of the humans' worst qualities is pride. He says that " 'they need very little provocation to become boastful toads.' " Explain what you think this means. Do you think Zeus is right? Why or why not?

5. Read the "Insights" section following the myth to find out more about Prometheus. Does this information confirm or change your opinion about his character? Explain.

6. Discuss the traits of Zeus and Hephaestus. What is your opinion of these two gods now that you have read the myth? Which one is more to blame for the harm done to Prometheus? Explain.

### Written or oral reports

1. Below is a list of people who have disobeyed the law in order to help others. Pick one of these people, learn more about him or her, and compare to Prometheus.
   a. Martin Luther King, Jr.
   b. Jesus Christ
   c. Harriet Tubman
   d. Nelson Mandela
   e. Joan of Arc

2. Many authors, musicians, and artists have been inspired by the story of Prometheus over the centuries. Find another work about Prometheus and report on it to the class. Tell how it relates to the myth of Prometheus. Some suggestions to look at, read, or listen to include
   a. *Prometheus in Chains on Mount Caucasus,* a painting by Peter Paul Rubens
   b. "Prometheus," a poem by George Gordon, Lord Byron
   c. *Promethee,* an opera by Gabriel Faure
   d. *Creatures of Prometheus,* a ballet by Ludwig van Beethoven
   e. "Prometheus' Poem of Fire," a symphonic poem by Alexander Scriabin

3. Read other Greek myths about the creation of humans. How do these myths differ? Which do you prefer? Why?

4. Read other stories about the creation of the human race. You might want to read the biblical account. Also, look at the Nordic, Indian, Chinese, Japanese, Egyptian, Mayan, Aztec, or Navajo stories.

### Creative writing activities

1. Imagine you are Prometheus. You want to ask Zeus face-to-face to give fire to humans. But before you visit him, you want to write a letter about this. Write the letter, telling Zeus why he should give fire to the humans. Give reasons that will convince Zeus to agree with you. (Offer different reasons than the ones stated in the myth.)

2. As Prometheus steals the coal from the gods' central fire, he refers to it as "a jewel fit for my humans." Write a poem about Prometheus' gift of fire based on this jewel image.

*continued*

3. Imagine you are seeing fire for the first time as Prometheus gives it to you. Write a brief account of this episode from your point of view.

4. Write your own sequel to Prometheus' story. Answer some or all of the following questions: How long is Prometheus chained to the mountain? Who sets him free? Do Prometheus' predictions come true?

## Artistic activities

1. Make a collage of the gifts Prometheus gave humans. You may want to include the gifts of life and fire, but show other gifts as well.

2. Cave-dwellers once drew pictures on the walls of their caves to show important events in their lives. Imagine you live in a cave. Sketch several cave-drawings which tell the story of Prometheus giving fire to humans.

3. Draw a scene from the myth which includes Prometheus and Zeus. Show these two characters as you think they might look and act.

4. Make a clay sculpture of one of the characters from the myth. Give a title to your sculpture, and display it for the rest of the class to see.

## Small-group discussion

1. In the myth, Prometheus knows what his fate will be when he gives fire to humans. What would be the advantages and disadvantages of knowing your fate? How would it affect your actions and outlook? If you had the choice, would you choose to know your fate or not? Explain.

2. Review Hephaestus' actions in the myth. Then list alternatives Hephaestus could have taken. Also, give the consequences for each alternative.

## THE TWELVE LABORS OF HERACLES

# PREREADING ACTIVITIES

### Story Themes

Several themes of "The Twelve Labors of Heracles" are listed below. They will help you prepare activities which will stimulate students' interest and involvement in the story.

1.) A strong and willing spirit is needed to succeed against great odds.
2.) To accomplish great tasks takes self-control.
3.) Common sense and cleverness are as important as intelligence.
4.) Even unpleasant experiences can have positive outcomes.
5.) Obstacles are more easily overcome if met one at a time.

### Spotlight on Vocabulary
### [Guided Practice]

*Objective:*

The learner will demonstrate an understanding of ten vocabulary words by showing which word belongs in each of ten sentences.

*Skill level:*

Knowledge/recall; application

*Description:*

This exercise introduces students to ten words in the story which may be new to them. First students preview the words and their definitions. Then they use the words to complete ten sentences.

The sentences discuss topics familiar to most students, so they can see how the new words fit into their existing web of knowledge. The goal of the exercise is to help students read the story more easily. Complete mastery of the vocabulary words at this stage is not expected.

*Suggestion:*

If prereading vocabulary work is kept short, word study can build interest without dampening enthusiasm. Exposure to these ten selected words will give students a head start toward understanding the story. A *postreading* vocabulary check and suggestions for further vocabulary study are provided for use *after* students have read the story.

### Setting the Stage
### [Anticipatory Set]

*Objective:*

The learner will demonstrate an understanding of the effects of anger in his or her own life by writing about a personal experience. The learner will also demonstrate an understanding of loyalty by describing, defining, and relating a personal experience.

*Skill level:*

Analysis; application

*Description:*

First students are asked to describe a time when they lost their temper and tell what happened as a result. Then they are asked to give personal meanings and definitions of loyalty and to write about an example of misplaced loyalty.

*Suggestion:*

Have students share their experiences of anger and misplaced loyalty. What are the similarities and differences in their experiences?

# THE TWELVE LABORS OF HERACLES

## POSTREADING ACTIVITIES

### It Happened Like This
### [Check for Understanding]

*Objective:*

The learner will demonstrate comprehension of the story by correctly answering ten multiple-choice questions.

*Skill level:*

Knowledge; comprehension

*Description:*

This exercise tests recall of important facts in the story. Students identify, from three choices, the answer that correctly completes each of ten sentences.

*Suggestion:*

Page number references on the response key show where the answer to each question can be found. These page numbers can be given to students who are taking an open-book test. The page numbers are also helpful when discussing the quiz after papers have been corrected.

### Vocabulary Review
### [Check for Understanding]

*Objective:*

The learner will demonstrate an understanding of ten words by identifying the correct synonym for each.

*Skill level:*

Knowledge

*Description:*

This exercise tests mastery of the ten words introduced in the **Spotlight on Vocabulary** exercise. The words are presented in the context of sentences taken directly from the story. Students identify, from three choices, the correct synonym for each word.

*Suggestion:*

Results of the vocabulary check will show which words students find most difficult. You may wish to provide further reinforcement for problem words.

### Literary Focus: The Making of a Hero
### [Guided or Independent Practice]

*Objective:*

The learner will demonstrate an understanding of the qualities which enabled Heracles to accomplish heroic tasks by analyzing six tasks. The learner will then demonstrate an understanding of the Greeks' idea of heroism by making inferences based on his or her knowledge of Heracles.

*Skill level:*

Analysis; evaluation

*Description:*

Students will first select tasks and then fill in a chart listing the tasks and what physical ability, personality trait, and mental skill Heracles shows in accomplishing each one. Next students will use the chart to draw conclusions about what makes Heracles a hero. They will identify his strengths and weaknesses and decide which qualities were most admired by the Greeks.

*Suggestion:*

Have students compare and contrast Heracles with some modern-day heroes and decide how today's heroes differ from yesterday's.

### The Reading-Writing Connection:
### Unlocking Passages
### [Guided or Independent Practice]

*Objective:*

The learner will demonstrate an ability to make inferences by answering questions based on quotations from the story.

*Skill level:*

Comprehension; application; analysis

*continued*

# THE TWELVE LABORS OF HERACLES

*Description:*

First students read a quotation; then they answer three questions about the quote. The first question requires an interpretation of the quote. The second question requires an inference. The third question, to be answered in a journal entry, asks students to relate the quotation to their personal experience.

The questions are intended to lead students to greater understanding and appreciation of the story. The questions also allow students to bridge the gap between their own knowledge and story concepts.

Quotation 1 concerns Heracles' need to control his temper. Quotation 2 concerns his lack of respect for a coward. Quotation 3 concerns Heracles' resentment at having his intelligence ridiculed.

*Suggestion:*

Make the questions the subject of a small-group or class discussion.

## Writing Corner: A Letter to Eurystheus
## [Extending Students' Thinking]

*Objective:*

The learner will demonstrate an ability to write from another's point of view by writing a letter from Heracles to Eurystheus.

*Skill level:*

Synthesis; evaluation

*Description:*

First students take on Heracles' point of view and answer questions about his thoughts while completing his labors, the lessons he learned, and what advice he would give to Eurystheus. Then, on a separate piece of paper, students are asked to write a letter from Heracles to the prince, telling him about the value of the labors and then giving him some princely advice.

*Suggestion:*

Have students volunteer to read their letters to Eurystheus. They may wish to pair up and dramatize their readings. In that case, one student would play the part of Heracles; the other would play Eurystheus' role.

## One Step Further
## [Extending Students' Thinking]

*Objective:*

The learner will demonstrate an ability to interpret, compare, contrast, and/or create by participating in discussions, preparing reports, or completing special projects.

*Skill level:*

Application; analysis; synthesis; evaluation

*Description:*

Students choose from an array of suggested follow-up activities which will help them process the story and respond creatively to the story's conflicts and themes. The activities encourage students of varying abilities to employ higher-level thinking skills.

*Suggestion:*

You may wish to use this page as a teacher reference and assign projects to individuals or groups. However the page may also be reproduced so that students can select their own topics.

Although the suggested activities are divided into categories such as **Class discussion** and **Written or oral reports**, most of the topics can be adapted for use in many ways.

# THE TWELVE LABORS OF HERACLES

## SPOTLIGHT ON VOCABULARY

Study the words and meanings shown in the box.
Then complete each sentence below by writing the
correct word on the line.

| | |
|---|---|
| **agitated**—disturbed; restless | **mulled**—thought over; considered |
| **distract**—draw attention away; | carefully |
| sidetrack | **penance**—act done to make up for |
| **foul**—disgusting | a sin; punishment taken |
| **gaped**—stared in surprise | **quivered**—trembled; shook |
| **intruder**—unwelcome guest; | **stature**—size; height |
| invader | **wary**—cautious; very careful |

1. Angelo _____ in wonder at the magician's tricks.

2. The anxious fans became _____ and began yelling
   angrily when they learned the game was sold out.

3. Quang _____ over the good and bad points about
   buying the car before he came to a decision.

4. The _____ who visited the hen house every night
   proved to be a raccoon stealing eggs.

5. Maria was _____ about climbing the ladder because
   she had once fallen off one.

6. Mitchell had the perfect _____ for playing basketball,
   but he didn't have the skills to match his height.

7. Lu smelled the _____ odor of old, rotting garbage.

8. Because any noise could easily _____ her, Edith wore
   earplugs when she did homework.

9. The campers _____ in fear when they heard the two
   bears approach their tent.

10. Tom Sawyer's _____ for disobeying Aunt Polly was
    to whitewash the fence.

# THE TWELVE LABORS OF HERACLES

## SETTING THE STAGE

These questions will help you get ready to read "The Twelve Labors of Heracles." Prepare to discuss the questions by jotting down answers on the lines.

1. Heracles, the hero of the story, has many good qualities. However, he has one great fault: a hot temper. Sometimes his temper helps him, but usually it causes serious problems.

    Now think about your own temper.

    a. Describe a time when you lost your temper.

    _____

    _____

    _____

    _____

    _____

    _____

    b. Did you solve a problem or create a problem by losing your temper? Explain your answer.

    _____

    _____

    _____

    _____

    _____

    _____

*continued*

c. On the whole, is it healthy to lose your temper? Or is it troublesome and unhealthy? Explain your response.

_____

_____

_____

_____

_____

_____

2. Heracles believes in being loyal. He is even loyal to a prince whom he does not like or respect.

     Consider what loyalty means to you.

a. Give three examples of loyalty.

_____

_____

_____

_____

_____

_____

*continued*

b. Now give your definition of loyalty.

_____

_____

_____

_____

_____

_____

c. Describe a time when you or someone you know was loyal to a person or cause that did not deserve it. Tell why you or the other person remained loyal.

_____

_____

_____

_____

_____

_____

Name _____

## IT HAPPENED LIKE THIS

Write the letter of the best answer on the line.

_____ 1. Hera is jealous of Heracles because he is
a. stronger than she is.
b. the son of her husband, Zeus, and a mortal woman.
c. destined to take Zeus' throne some day.

_____ 2. Apollo's oracle commands Heracles to serve for twelve years after Heracles
a. kills his wife and children.
b. steals the Golden Apples from the Hesperides.
c. conquers Diomedes, king of Thrace.

_____ 3. Heracles kills the Lion of Nemea by
a. shooting an arrow into the lion's heart.
b. choking the lion to death.
c. beating the lion with his club.

_____ 4. Iolaus uses a hot branding iron to
a. sear the Hydra's necks.
b. frighten the man-eating mares of Diomedes.
c. brand the Cretan bull.

_____ 5. Heracles is given only one day to
a. find the Golden Apples.
b. clean the stables of King Augeas.
c. capture the great boar.

_____ 6. The birds of Stymphalus attack after Heracles
a. sets fire to their marsh with Helios' torch.
b. destroys a nest of young birds.
c. shakes the brass rattle Athena had given him.

_____ 7. When Hera takes the form of an Amazon, she
a. helps Heracles steal the belt of Hippolyta.
b. convinces the women to attack Heracles.
c. urges Hippolyta not to marry Heracles.

_____ 8. Because he doesn't want to hold up the sky forever, Heracles
a. asks Iolaus to take a turn.
b. gives the sky to Prometheus.
c. tricks Atlas into taking back the heavens.

_____ 9. Heracles refuses to be defeated when sent to Hades because he
a. is too close to freedom to give up.
b. wants to beat Hera.
c. feels Cerberus will be no challenge.

_____10. Heracles claims that his service to Eurystheus has taught him how to
a. be patient and brave.
b. trust the gods and fate.
c. control his temper and strength.

**POSTREADING**

# THE TWELVE LABORS OF HERACLES

## VOCABULARY REVIEW

These sentences are taken from the story. Circle the answer that comes closest in meaning to each word in **dark type**.

1. "Heracles had to be particularly **wary** of Hera, Zeus' queen. This powerful goddess was always jealous. . . . "
   - a. afraid
   - b. cautious
   - c. demanding

2. "[Heracles] was soon much stronger and taller than other young men. But with this strength and **stature** came a hot temper."
   - a. size
   - b. attitude
   - c. imagination

3. " . . . Heracles learned from the oracle that to make up for the crime, he must serve Eurystheus for twelve years. . . . it was his **penance** to serve Eurystheus."
   - a. punishment
   - b. luck
   - c. duty

4. "Then the hero **gaped** at what he saw. The club had shattered into a hundred pieces."
   - a. laughed
   - b. wondered
   - c. stared

5. "The sharp nip of that tiny creature was enough to **distract** Heracles."
   - a. persuade
   - b. sidetrack
   - c. anger

6. "The **foul** birds carried terrible diseases and tore the flesh off any living creature."
   - a. disgusting
   - b. hungry
   - c. daring

7. "Heracles **mulled** over his task."
   - a. cried
   - b. thought
   - c. prayed

8. "At the sight of the returning hero, Eurystheus grew very **agitated**."
   - a. relieved
   - b. interested
   - c. disturbed

9. "Heracles gasped when he felt the great weight. His feet sank in the earth and he **quivered**."
   - a. trembled
   - b. disappeared
   - c. obeyed

10. "He came spitting and growling with all three of his heads. But the dog stopped short when he saw the **intruder**."
    - a. criminal
    - b. invader
    - c. monster

RETOLD CLASSIC MYTHS, VOL. 1
Copyright 1990. Perfection Learning Corporation, Logan, Iowa 51546

# THE TWELVE LABORS OF HERACLES

## LITERARY FOCUS: THE MAKING OF A HERO

Heracles was considered to be one of the greatest of all the Greek heroes. As a result, he appears in many legends and tales. "The Twelve Labors of Heracles" is only one account of the hero's many adventures. However, the story does provide many examples of his heroic qualities.

The following chart will help you examine the qualities Heracles shows when he undertakes the twelve labors. Select five of the heroic tasks and then complete the chart. Decide what physical ability, personality trait, and mental skill Heracles shows for each labor that you select. The first section has been done for you.

| HERACLES' LABOR | PHYSICAL ABILITY | PERSONALITY TRAIT | MENTAL SKILL |
|---|---|---|---|
| 1. *brings back the skin of the lion of Nemea* | *chokes the lion with his bare hands* | *fearlessness* | *cleverness* |
| 2. | | | |
| 3. | | | |
| 4. | | | |
| 5. | | | |
| 6. | | | |

*continued*

Name _____

## Summing up

Use information from your chart to answer the following questions about what makes Heracles a hero.

1. What are Heracles' strengths and weaknesses? Explain your response.

   _____

   _____

   _____

   _____

2. What heroic qualities do you think the Greeks valued most about Heracles? Explain your response.

   _____

   _____

   _____

   _____

3. Do you agree with the Greeks? Why or why not? What heroic qualities would you add or change?

   _____

   _____

   _____

   _____

Name _____

# THE TWELVE LABORS OF HERACLES

## THE READING-WRITING CONNECTION: UNLOCKING PASSAGES

Answer the questions about these quotes taken from "The Twelve Labors of Heracles." (Go back to the story if you need more clues.) Write your response to part *c* of each question on a separate sheet of paper.

1. "Heracles' family knew he would master great things in the future. But they also knew he first had to master his temper." (page 32)

   a. What does the passage mean as used in the story?

   _____

   _____

   b. Explain why it was important for Heracles to master his temper. Give an example from the story to support your opinion.

   _____

   _____

   _____

   _____

   c. **Journal writing:** Describe a time when you didn't control your temper and you got into trouble.

2. "Many guards stood close by, ready to do all the prince's fighting for him. Heracles couldn't respect a man like that." (pages 33-34)

   a. What does the passage mean as used in the story?

   _____

   _____

*continued*

b. Why wouldn't Heracles respect Prince Eurystheus? What kind of a person would Heracles admire?

_____

_____

_____

_____

c. **Journal writing:** What are your feelings about people who have other people fight their battles for them? Are these people smart or cowardly? Explain.

3. "Heracles might joke about his own intelligence. But he resented it when others made fun of him." (page 39)

a. What does the passage mean as used in the story?

_____

_____

b. Where else in the story is Heracles made fun of for his lack of intelligence? Do you think he truly acts stupidly? If not, why else is he mocked? Explain your response.

_____

_____

_____

_____

c. **Journal writing:** Describe a time when someone made fun of you or someone you know. How did you or the person you know react?

# THE TWELVE LABORS OF HERACLES

## WRITING CORNER:
## A LETTER TO EURYSTHEUS

Heracles says that after twelve years of service to Eurystheus, he thinks he has " 'found how to control [his] temper and strength.' " Although Heracles would admit that these were not easy lessons to learn, he is grateful for the experience.

Imagine that you are Heracles. You have decided to write a letter to Eurystheus about the value of your experiences.

First answer these questions to help prepare you to write the letter.

1. Even though you did not like Eurystheus from the beginning, why did you continue to serve him?

_____

_____

_____

2. What did you think about Eurystheus when you had completed your twelve labors?

_____

_____

_____

3. The major lesson you learned was to control your temper and strength. Why was that so important for you to learn?

_____

_____

_____

*continued*

4.   What other specific lessons did you learn from some of the labors?

_____

_____

_____

5.   What advice would you like to give Eurystheus?

_____

_____

_____

On a separate sheet of paper, write your letter to Eurystheus. Remember to write the letter from Heracles' point of view. Tell the prince about the value of your labors. Also give advice to the prince.

## ONE STEP FURTHER

### Class discussion

1. Many of Heracles' problems arise because Hera interferes. Give examples where Hera causes problems for Heracles. How might Heracles' life have been different if the goddess had left him alone?

2. Heracles does not complete all of his labors alone. Give examples of this from the story. Does receiving help suggest that Heracles is weak? Explain your response.

3. Heracles states that his " 'brain is a turtle.' " What does he mean by this? Give instances in the story that support Heracles' statement. Are there times when Heracles is quick thinking as well? If so, give examples.

4. Why does Heracles call Eurystheus a coward? What other opinions does Heracles express about the prince? Are Heracles' opinions justified? Explain.

5. What does Eurystheus mean when he says that Heracles will have no trouble "relating" to horses. Why do you think Eurystheus makes fun of Heracles? Do you agree or disagree with the prince? Explain. Does Heracles make fun of himself? Why or why not?

6. Although Heracles is sent to get the man-eating mares of Diomedes, he also frees the citizens of Thrace. How does he accomplish this task? What does this action suggest about Heracles' character?

7. At first, Hippolyta agrees to give Heracles her belt. But soon she and the other Amazons turn against Heracles, and Heracles kills her. Why? How does Heracles react to killing Hippolyta? Why?

8. Why does Heracles think his twelfth labor is a death sentence? Would you have been disappointed if Heracles had not accepted or completed his twelfth labor? Explain your response.

### Written or oral reports

1. Some of Heracles' twelve labors have been shown in Greek art. There are statues, pottery, and metal work that picture Heracles' labors. Ask your librarian to help you find photos of these pieces of art. Then prepare a report about how Heracles' heroism was reflected in Greek art. If possible, bring the photos to class to share with your classmates.

2. Read about another one of Heracles' adventures and how he performed good deeds. Compare his actions and character traits with the ones you just read about in this story. Be prepared to share your findings with your classmates.

3. Heracles' strength is repeatedly emphasized. Nothing alive could defeat him. Only supernatural forces could overcome him. Even his death shows his strength. Because death would not come for him, he went to death. Find the story of Heracles' death and report the details to your classmates.

### Creative writing activities

1. Imagine that Heracles kept a diary during his twelve years of service to Eurystheus. Select one of the twelve labors. Then write the entry that Heracles would have written after completing the task.

2. Suppose the original title of the story was "The Thirteen Labors of Heracles," but the last part of the story was lost. What kind of labor would you send Heracles on as his thirteenth mission? Create another tough task for Heracles to complete. Then write the story of his thirteenth labor.

*continued*

3. Imagine that while visiting in the Underworld, Heracles has an opportunity to be reunited with his wife and children. Write your version of this reunion.

## Artistic activities

1. Draw Heracles in one of these scenes from the story.
   a. Wearing the Lion of Nemea's skin
   b. Slaying the Hydra
   c. Shooting arrows at the birds of Stymphalus
   d. Having dinner with Hippolyta
   e. Shooting the monster Geryon

2. Because he is the strongest man in the world, it would only seem natural that Heracles might make a guest appearance at a world weightlifting championship. Design a poster for this event that will feature Heracles giving a special demonstration of his physical strength.

3. Suppose that your class is designing a mythology calendar. Each month will feature a different god, goddess, hero, or heroine. Your assignment is to select the month that best represents Heracles and draw the illustration for that month.

4. Originally, Greek drama used masks to portray different characters. Select a character from the story and make a mask for your class production of "The Twelve Labors of Heracles."

## Small-group activities

1. Watch some movie and cartoon versions of Heracles' life. Write reviews of these and rate them with stars—five stars being the best presentation. Then share your reviews with the class. You may choose to do this by hosting a "talk show" or by publishing the reviews.

2. Select a scene or two from the story and prepare a pantomime. You might choose some music that fits the scene and its mood. Then write a script for a narrator to read while the rest of the group mimes.

# CIRCE AND ODYSSEUS

# PREREADING ACTIVITIES

### Story Themes

Several themes of "Circe and Odysseus" are listed below. They will help you prepare activities which will stimulate students' interest and involvement in the story.

1.) It takes keen perception to detect trickery and deceit.
2.) Sometimes it is best to trust your instincts.
3.) A leader has a responsibility to safeguard his followers.
4.) Hope can sustain you through times of hardship.
5.) A person's desire for home is a powerful force. ("There's no place like home.")

### Spotlight on Vocabulary
### [Guided Practice]

*Objective:*

The learner will demonstrate an understanding of ten vocabulary words by showing which word belongs in each of ten sentences.

*Skill level:*

Knowledge/recall; application

*Description:*

This exercise introduces students to ten words in the story which may be new to them. First students preview the words and their definitions. Then they use the words to complete ten sentences.

The sentences discuss topics familiar to most students, so they can see how the new words fit into their existing web of knowledge. The goal of the exercise is to help students read the story more easily. Complete mastery of the vocabulary words at this stage is not expected.

*Suggestion:*

If prereading vocabulary work is kept short, word study can build interest without dampening enthusiasm. Exposure to these ten selected words will give students a head start toward understanding the story. A *postreading* vocabulary check and suggestions for further vocabulary study are provided for use *after* students have read the story.

### Setting the Stage
### [Anticipatory Set]

*Objective:*

The learner will demonstrate an understanding of leadership qualities by listing and evaluating these traits and writing a description of the ideal leader. The learner will also show an understanding of the character traits of a witch by identifying and discussing the qualities possessed by the typical witch.

*Skill level:*

Analysis; synthesis; application

*Description:*

First students are asked to list four qualities which they think a leader should possess and tell why each quality is important. Then students use this list to write their own definitions of the ideal leader. After reading the myth, they are to determine how closely Odysseus fits their definitions.

In a second activity, students study a checklist of character traits and choose those which fit their idea of a typical witch. After reading they are asked to compare Circe to their idea of a typical witch.

*Suggestion:*

Have students use their definitions of the ideal leader to determine how they would evaluate past and present political, economic, and social leaders.

## CIRCE AND ODYSSEUS

## POSTREADING ACTIVITIES

### It Happened Like This
#### [Check for Understanding]
*Objective:*

The learner will demonstrate comprehension of the story by correctly answering ten multiple-choice questions.

*Skill level:*

Knowledge; comprehension

*Description:*

This exercise tests recall of important facts in the story. Students identify, from three choices, the answer that correctly completes each of ten sentences.

*Suggestion:*

Page number references on the response key show where the answer to each question can be found. These page numbers can be given to students who are taking an open-book test. The page numbers are also helpful when discussing the quiz after papers have been corrected.

### Vocabulary Review
#### [Check for Understanding]
*Objective:*

The learner will demonstrate an understanding of ten words by identifying the correct synonym for each.

*Skill level:*

Knowledge

*Description:*

This exercise tests mastery of the ten words introduced in the **Spotlight on Vocabulary** exercise. The words are presented in the context of sentences taken directly from the story. Students identify, from three choices, the correct synonym for each word.

*Suggestion:*

Results of the vocabulary check will show which words students find most difficult.

You may wish to provide further reinforcement for problem words.

### Literary Focus: Character Foils
#### [Guided or Independent Practice]
*Objective:*

The learner will demonstrate an understanding of how character foils are used to help define personalities by comparing Odysseus with his foil, Eurylochus.

*Skill level:*

Analysis; evaluation

*Description:*

Students are given a chart listing five qualities and are asked to consider these qualities in Odysseus and Eurylochus. Next they list examples showing the differences between the two men as evidenced by these character traits. Finally they determine if there are examples that show Odysseus is the better leader. And they decide which of Eurylochus' qualities, if any, Odysseus lacks.

*Suggestion:*

Have students choose a figure they admire, either a character from literature or a real person. Ask them to identify the dominant personality traits of the person they have chosen. Then have them write a personality sketch of a person who could be a foil for this figure.

### The Reading-Writing Connection:
### Unlocking Passages
#### [Guided or Independent Practice]
*Objective:*

The learner will demonstrate an ability to make inferences by answering questions based on quotations from the story.

*Skill level:*

Comprehension; application; analysis

*continued*

# CIRCE AND ODYSSEUS

*Description:*

First students read a quotation; then they answer three questions about the quote. The first question requires an interpretation of the quote. The second question requires an inference. The third question, to be answered in a journal entry, asks students to relate the quotation to their personal experience.

The questions are intended to lead students to greater understanding and appreciation of the story. The questions also allow students to bridge the gap between their own knowledge and story concepts.

Quotation 1 concerns the contrast between Eurylochus' report of events at Circe's house and the seeming calm Odysseus encounters there. Quotation 2 concerns Eurylochus' reluctance to follow Odysseus to Circe's home. Quotation 3 concerns Odysseus' advice to Eurylochus to trust in the gods and in himself.

*Suggestion:*

Make the questions the subject of a small-group or class discussion.

## Writing Corner: The Gods Step In
### [Extending Students' Thinking]

*Objective:*

The learner will demonstrate an understanding of the use of magic in the myth by preparing to write an original myth in which the gods use magic to help or hinder a hero.

*Skill level:*

Analysis; synthesis

*Description:*

First students choose a general plan for their myth from a list of suggestions. (If they wish, they may devise their own plans.) Next students are guided to identify and describe the characters, setting, and plot details for their myth. This outline can then be used to write a rough draft of the myth. Students may then meet with classmates to revise their stories before writing their final version.

*Suggestion:*

Have students compile their myths into a classroom anthology to be shared with other students.

## One Step Further
### [Extending Students' Thinking]

*Objective:*

The learner will demonstrate an ability to interpret, compare, contrast, and/or create by participating in discussions, preparing reports, or completing special projects.

*Skill level:*

Application; analysis; synthesis; evaluation

*Description:*

Students choose from an array of suggested follow-up activities which will help them process the story and respond creatively to the story's conflicts and themes. The activities encourage students of varying abilities to employ higher-level thinking skills.

*Suggestion:*

You may wish to use this page as a teacher reference and assign projects to individuals or groups. However the page may also be reproduced so that students can select their own topics.

Although the suggested activities are divided into categories such as **Class discussion** and **Written or oral reports**, most of the topics can be adapted for use in many ways.

# CIRCE AND ODYSSEUS

## SPOTLIGHT ON VOCABULARY

Study the words and meanings shown in the box.
Then complete each sentence below by writing the
correct word on the line.

| | |
|---|---|
| **conferred**—discussed; consulted | **impish**—devilish; full of pranks |
| **cower**—crouch fearfully | **poised**—balanced; steadied |
| **dense**—thick; crowded | **recoiled**—jumped back |
| **elapsed**—passed by | **sty**—pigpen |
| **hazardous**—dangerous; risky | **sullen**—cross; angry |

1. At graduation, Adrian held the microphone _____ in front of her, ready to give her speech.

2. The senator was so stunned by the reporter's question that a full minute _____ before she answered.

3. The _____, overgrown jungle hid the crashed plane from the search party.

4. Lee's practical jokes and _____ tricks often get him into trouble.

5. Anthony _____ and nearly tripped over a log behind him when he saw the big snake in his path.

6. At least once a month, my parents complain that my messy bedroom looks like (a, an) _____.

7. Kim looked _____ and irritated when her dad refused to let her borrow the car.

8. My cowardly dog, Fox, will always _____ under my bed when a thunderstorm passes through.

9. The ice and snow made the road _____, forcing traffic to move very slowly.

10. Because his father was a mechanic, Luis _____ with him before buying a car.

# CIRCE AND ODYSSEUS

## SETTING THE STAGE

These questions will help you get ready to read "Circe and Odysseus." Prepare to discuss the questions by jotting down answers on the lines.

1. The main character, Odysseus, has many leadership qualities. One of those qualities is putting the safety of his men before his own.

   a. List four other qualities that you think a leader should possess. Briefly tell why you think each quality is important.

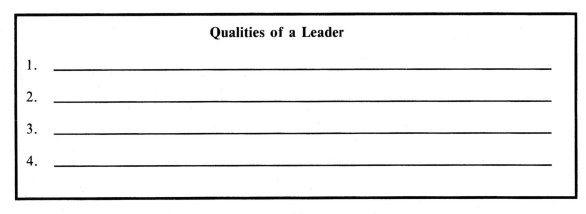

   **Qualities of a Leader**

   1. _____
   2. _____
   3. _____
   4. _____

   b. Now use the qualities you listed to write your definition of a leader.

   _____
   _____
   _____
   _____

   c. After you read the myth, compare your ideal leader to Odysseus. Does Odysseus fit your definition? Why or why not?

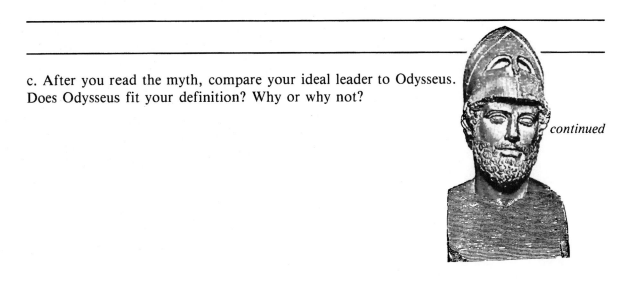

*continued*

2. One of the main characters in the story—Circe—is a witch. Think of some witches you know of from TV, movies, or other stories.

a. Now check off the traits below that fit your idea of a typical witch.

| | |
|---|---|
| _____ intelligent | _____ mischievous |
| _____ kind | _____ cowardly |
| _____ evil | _____ lonely |
| _____ beautiful | _____ vengeful |
| _____ hideous | _____ stupid |
| _____ fascinating | _____ fearless |
| _____ disgusting | _____ young |
| _____ forgiving | _____ old |

b. Once you complete your list, discuss your responses with a partner or group. Use examples of other witches to illustrate the traits of your ideal witch.

c. After you finish the story, return to your checklist. Which of the qualities you checked does Circe have? Which of your traits should she have that she doesn't possess?

RETOLD CLASSIC MYTHS, VOL. 1

Copyright 1990. Perfection Learning Corporation, Logan, Iowa 51546

Name _____

## IT HAPPENED LIKE THIS

Write the letter of the best answer on the line.

_____ 1. At the beginning of the myth, Odysseus is troubled because he
   a. sees a storm on the horizon.
   b. believes he has failed as a leader.
   c. thinks Zeus has tricked him.

_____ 2. Eurylochus is upset because Odysseus and his crew have been trying to
   a. reach Ithaca for years.
   b. return to Troy.
   c. fool the gods.

_____ 3. While exploring the island, Odysseus sees a
   a. house with a smoking chimney.
   b. village of giants.
   c. herd of wild boars.

_____ 4. Eurylochus suspects there is danger at Circe's house because her
   a. windows have bars.
   b. lions and wolves are tame.
   c. singing makes the men sleepy.

_____ 5. Odysseus goes to Circe's house alone because
   a. he doesn't want to lose any more men.
   b. the crew refuses to go.
   c. Eurylochus won't let anyone go with Odysseus.

_____ 6. Hermes reveals that Circe has
   a. caused Odysseus' men to believe they are dead.
   b. made Odysseus' men think they are back home.
   c. changed Odysseus' men into pigs.

_____ 7. Hermes has Odysseus eat the moly because it will
   a. give Odysseus courage.
   b. keep Odysseus awake.
   c. shield Odysseus from magic.

_____ 8. Odysseus overcomes Circe and makes her
   a. burn down her house of magic.
   b. swear she'll cast no more spells.
   c. tell him the way home.

_____ 9. After Odysseus' men recover, they decide to
   a. leave at once for Ithaca.
   b. live on the island forever.
   c. stay with Circe for a time.

_____ 10. The gods advise Odysseus to
   a. seek the dead prophet Teiresias.
   b. wait a year before going home.
   c. leave Eurylochus behind.

## VOCABULARY REVIEW

These sentences are taken from the story. Circle the answer that comes closest in meaning to each word in **dark type**.

1. " 'What do you think hope is, Eurylochus?' asked Odysseus. 'A map,' he replied in a **sullen** voice.' "
       a. defeated      b. humble      c. cross

2. "His men followed him into the **dense** woods."
       a. thick      b. green      c. savage

3. "When the lions and wolves looked up, he **recoiled**. But the beasts remained still."
       a. jumped back      b. slumped down      c. ran forward

4. " 'I'm afraid she elected to make your men pigs. They're in her **sty** right now, digging in the mud.' "
       a. cellar      b. pen      c. cave

5. " 'Rush toward her as if you might kill her. She will **cower** and ask for mercy.' "
       a. move carefully    b. turn quickly      c. crouch fearfully

6. "At once Odysseus leapt up. In a moment, he had his sword **poised** at her throat."
       a. lowered      b. steadied      c. thrust

7. " 'I know this journey has been long and **hazardous** for you and your men.' "
       a. hopeless      b. dangerous      c. lonely

8. "Odysseus **conferred** with his men. In the end, they all agreed to stay."
       a. consulted      b. interfered      c. argued

9. "Days passed and slid into months. In fact, a full year **elapsed** before any of them noticed."
       a. returned      b. remained      c. passed

10. "An **impish** smile rose to Circe's lips."
       a. loving      b. devilish      c. concerned

# CIRCE AND ODYSSEUS

## LITERARY FOCUS: CHARACTER FOILS

A character's personality can be shown in many different ways. For example, a character's actions, words, and thoughts all reveal his or her personality.

A character's relationships with others can also give insights into personality. Using a *foil*—a character with a contrasting personality—is one way to develop a character. A contrast between the main character and the foil makes the main character's qualities easier to see.

In the myth "Circe and Odysseus," Eurylochus is a foil for Odysseus. On the chart below, list examples to show differences between Odysseus and Eurylochus. Note that one character may show one quality, while the other lacks that quality.

|  | Odysseus | Eurylochus |
|---|---|---|
| 1. Common sense |  |  |
| 2. Concern for others |  |  |
| 3. Bravery |  |  |
| 4. Respect given to him by others |  |  |
| 5. Sense of duty |  |  |

Now get together in small groups. Discuss the differences between Eurylochus and Odysseus. What examples can you give to prove that Odysseus is a better leader? Does Eurylochus have any qualities that Odysseus lacks? If so, what are they?

**POSTREADING**

## THE READING-WRITING CONNECTION: UNLOCKING PASSAGES

Answer the questions about these quotes taken from
"Circe and Odysseus." (Go back to the story if you
need more clues.) Write your response to part *c* of
each question on a separate sheet of paper.

1.  "It looked as calm and pleasant as ever. Eurylochus' tale seemed
    just a nightmare. Still, Odysseus knew all too well that many things
    are not what they seem." (page 62)

    a. What does the passage mean as used in the story?

    _____

    _____

    b. For a moment, Odysseus doubts Eurylochus. Is Odysseus justified
    in doubting Eurylochus' tale? Explain.

    _____

    _____

    _____

    c. **Journal writing:** Describe a time in your life when things were not
    what they seemed.

2.  "Eurylochus snorted. 'Maybe you're foolish enough to go,' he con-
    tinued. 'But I'm not! I remember the last time I followed Odysseus
    blindly. That day some of us ended up as a giant's dinner!' "
    (page 66)

    a. What does the passage mean as used in the story?

    _____

    _____

*continued*

RETOLD CLASSIC MYTHS, VOL. 1

b. What is Eurylochus afraid will happen? What reasons does he have to fear Circe?

_____

_____

_____

_____

c. **Journal writing:** Write about a time when you questioned someone's leadership. Did you continue to listen to or follow that person? Why or why not?

3. " 'There comes a point, my friend, when caution is lethal. Just as lethal as being reckless. Trust to the gods, Eurylochus. And your own wits.' " (page 66)

a. What does the passage mean as used in the story?

_____

_____

b. Does Odysseus always follow his own advice? What examples in the myth suggest that he trusts the gods? His wits?

_____

_____

_____

_____

c. **Journal writing:** Think about a time when you were reckless and a time when you were cautious. If you could relive the two situations, which of the two would you most want to change? Explain your response in your journal.

# CIRCE AND ODYSSEUS

## WRITING CORNER: THE GODS STEP IN

In "Circe and Odysseus," the gods both hinder and help Odysseus. For example, Circe casts a spell on Odysseus' men and turns them into pigs. In this scene, Circe's magic is used to create conflict. But with Hermes' help, Odysseus is able to save his men and turn Circe into a friend. So the gods both create and resolve conflict.

Create your own myth in which the gods use magic to hinder or help a hero. Complete the following activity to get started.

1. **The Plan**

   Choose a general plan for your myth. Check your choice or write your own.

   _____ A god uses magic to help a lost hero find the way home.

   _____ A god gives something magical to a hero to help him or her overcome a monster.

   _____ A hero is fighting an enemy, but some god uses magic to help the enemy.

   _____ A hero tries to help someone in need but is stopped by a god's magic.

   _____ Write your own: _____

   _____

2. **The Characters**

   a. Briefly describe the hero of your myth.

   _____

   _____

   _____

   b. Now list traits of the god who hinders or helps the hero.

   _____

   _____

   _____

RETOLD CLASSIC MYTHS, VOL. 1

c. List the other characters who will appear in the myth.

_____

_____

_____

3. **The Setting**

Briefly describe where your myth will take place.

_____

_____

_____

_____

4. **The Plot Details**

List four main events in your myth. Be sure that magic figures in the plot.

a. _____

_____

b. _____

_____

c. _____

_____

d. _____

_____

The final step is to write your myth. Use notes from your outline to write your first draft. Then have another classmate read your myth and make suggestions. Finally, revise your myth and present it to the class.

## ONE STEP FURTHER

### Class discussion

1. What does Eurylochus think of Odysseus? Is his opinion justified? Explain. What incident(s) in the story show that Odysseus is different than what Eurylochus thinks of him?

2. Why does Odysseus select Eurylochus to lead one of the groups of men? Do you think Odysseus' choice was a good one? Explain your response.

3. Discuss the relationship between Odysseus and Hermes. Do the two seem to know each other well? What do they appear to think of each other? Give evidence to support your responses.

4. When Odysseus returns to the ship, Eurylochus thinks Odysseus may be under Circe's spell. Why? If you were a member of Odysseus' crew, would you have believed or doubted Odysseus? Give reasons for your opinion.

5. Why do you think the gods want Circe to wait until Odysseus leaves before she gives him their advice? How do Odysseus and his men react to that advice? Judging from their reactions, what adventure awaits them?

### Written or oral reports

1. Find out more about Circe in an encyclopedia or other resource. Who is her father? Why is she on the island? Does she have children? Be prepared to share these and other details with your classmates.

2. Research witches in Greek mythology. Identify some witches and compare their powers to Circe. Did the Greeks view witches as basically good, evil, or a mix of both? How does the Greek idea of witches compare to the modern idea? Report your information to your classmates.

3. Find out about Odysseus' trip to the Underworld and his meeting with Teiresias. How does Odysseus encourage Teiresias to talk to him? What advice does Teiresias give to Odysseus? Be prepared to share this information with your classmates.

### Creative writing activities

1. Find out more information about ballads. Look for common subjects or themes, rhyme, and rhythm. Then write a ballad entitled "Circe the Sorceress."

2. Imagine that you are one of Odysseus' men who was turned into a pig. Write a humorous short story or diary entry that relates your experiences as a pig in Circe's sty. Give your story a clever title.

3. Write a scene in which Odysseus' men discuss their leader while he is away. You may also wish to have Odysseus overhear all or part of the discussion and give his reactions.

4. Imagine that you are a member of Odysseus' crew. Write a letter that you might place inside a bottle to float out to sea. Briefly describe the troubles of the crew and ask for help.

### Artistic activities

1. Suppose you want to stage this myth. Draw some sketches to show sets you would use for your play. Indicate background scenery, props, and entrances and exits.

2. Imagine that you work for a travel agent who specializes in sending clients on vacations to "living museums." These are museums where lifestyles of long ago are shown. Costumes, food, speech, and activities of the time are included in a living museum. One of the new trips the company sells is "A Greek

*continued*

Odyssey: Relive the Adventures of Odysseus.''
Your job is to draw up a museum floor plan.
Indicate in detail what you would include in
the museum. Also tell where your museum
would be located.

3. Draw a comic strip version of the myth.

## Small-group activities

1. Rewrite a scene from the myth as a drama.
Be sure to include dialogue. You may also wish
to write a script for a narrator. Then create

scenery and use props and costumes to stage
your scene. If possible, videotape your play to
show to other classes.

2. Create a scrapbook of Odysseus' adventure on Circe's island. Include photos,
souvenirs, and Odysseus' memories of the trip.

# AENEAS' TRIP TO THE UNDERWORLD

## PREREADING ACTIVITIES

### Story Themes

Several themes of "Aeneas' Trip to the Underworld" are listed below. They will help you prepare activities which will stimulate students' interest and involvement in the story.

1.) Sometimes things are not what they appear to be.
2.) Seek the help and advice of those who are wise when undertaking difficult adventures.
3.) It's good to have a guide in unknown territory.
4.) It sometimes takes great effort to turn dreams into reality.
5.) Persistence pays off.

### Spotlight on Vocabulary
### [Guided Practice]

*Objective:*
The learner will demonstrate an understanding of ten vocabulary words by showing which word belongs in each of ten sentences.

*Skill level:*
Knowledge/recall; application

*Description:*
This exercise introduces students to ten words in the story which may be new to them. First students preview the words and their definitions. Then they use the words to complete ten sentences.

The sentences discuss topics familiar to most students, so they can see how the new words fit into their existing web of knowledge. The goal of the exercise is to help students read the story more easily. Complete mastery of the vocabulary words at this stage is not expected.

*Suggestion:*
If prereading vocabulary work is kept short, word study can build interest without dampening enthusiasm. Exposure

to these ten selected words will give students a head start toward understanding the story. A *postreading* vocabulary check and suggestions for further vocabulary study are provided for use *after* students have read the story.

### Setting the Stage
### [Anticipatory Set]

*Objective:*
The learner will demonstrate an understanding of what it would be like to be homeless by answering questions from the viewpoint of a homeless person. The learner will also demonstrate an understanding of Aeneas' belief in an afterlife by selecting a deceased person he or she would like to communicate with and answering questions about an imagined conversation.

*Skill level:*
Analysis; evaluation

*Description:*
Imagining themselves as homeless people, students answer questions about how they would find a new home, what problems they might face, and what they would learn from the experience. Next they imagine that they can communicate with someone who has died. They will select a person, explain the selection, decide what questions they will ask, and tell what the person's response might be.

*Suggestion:*
As students discuss their answers, keep them focused on experiences and ideas they share. Students may find it helpful to read the myth in terms of Aeneas' human reactions to exile and his encounter with an alien world.

# AENEAS' TRIP TO THE UNDERWORLD

## POSTREADING ACTIVITIES

### It Happened Like This
### [Check for Understanding]

*Objective:*

The learner will demonstrate comprehension of the story by correctly answering ten multiple-choice questions.

*Skill level:*

Knowledge; comprehension

*Description:*

This exercise tests recall of important facts in the story. Students identify, from three choices, the answer that correctly completes each of ten sentences.

*Suggestion:*

Page number references on the response key show where the answer to each question can be found. These page numbers can be given to students who are taking an open-book test. The page numbers are also helpful when discussing the quiz after papers have been corrected.

### Vocabulary Review
### [Check for Understanding]

*Objective:*

The learner will demonstrate an understanding of ten words by identifying the correct synonym for each.

*Skill level:*

Knowledge

*Description:*

This exercise tests mastery of the ten words introduced in the **Spotlight on Vocabulary** exercise. The words are presented in the context of sentences taken directly from the story. Students identify, from three choices, the correct synonym for each word.

*Suggestion:*

Results of the vocabulary check will show which words students find most difficult. You may wish to provide further reinforcement for problem words.

### Literary Focus: Plot Devices
### [Guided or Independent Practice]

*Objective:*

The learner will demonstrate an understanding of how plot devices are used to move along the action of a story by investigating story situations and identifying either the plot device used or the plot action that results.

*Skill level:*

Analysis; evaluation

*Description:*

This activity is in gameboard format. Nine difficulties encountered in the story are listed. For each obstacle either the plot device used or the resulting plot advancement is given. Students then complete the relationship by identifying and writing in the part that is missing.

*Suggestion:*

It may be helpful to discuss cause-and-effect relationships before doing this exercise. Help students to see a plot device as a cause of story advancement.

Students may enjoy working on this activity in teams of two, taking turns moving along the gameboard by answering questions.

### The Reading-Writing Connection:
### Unlocking Passages
### [Guided or Independent Practice]

*Objective:*

The learner will demonstrate an ability to make inferences by answering questions based on quotations from the story.

*Skill level:*

Comprehension; application; analysis

*continued*

# AENEAS' TRIP TO THE UNDERWORLD

*Description:*

First students read a quotation; then they answer three questions about the quote. The first question requires an interpretation of the quote. The second question requires an inference. The third question, to be answered in a journal entry, asks students to relate the quotation to their personal experience or views.

The questions are intended to lead students to greater understanding and appreciation of the story. The questions also allow students to bridge the gap between their own knowledge and story concepts.

Quotation 1 concerns Aeneas' desire to find a new home for the Trojans. Quotation 2 concerns the Sibyl's plea for entrance into the Underworld. Quotation 3 concerns the Sibyl's reassurance that Palinurus will receive a proper burial.

*Suggestion:*

Make the questions the subject of small-group or class discussion.

## Writing Corner: Creating a World
## [Extending Students' Thinking]

*Objective:*

The learner will demonstrate an understanding of the elements needed to create a fictional world (setting, characters, action, and mood) by creating descriptions of their own imaginary world.

*Skill level:*

Application; synthesis

*Description:*

First students decide on the basic setting of a fictional world. Then they are asked to describe the physical aspects of the setting—how it will look, feel, sound, and smell. Next students describe the overall traits of the inhabitants and write some

of the usual activities in this world. Students will then identify the mood. Finally, they will write a description for their world using these details.

*Suggestion:*

Before students tackle this activity, discuss the importance of using specific details to help readers/listeners visualize this new world. Then when students complete the activity, have them share their fictional worlds.

As a related activity, ask students to generate lists of details to describe their school or community to a stranger (or extraterrestrial). Use the same four categories of setting, characters, action, and mood. The class may then want to write a group description of this common world.

## One Step Further
## [Extending Students' Thinking]

*Objective:*

The learner will demonstrate an ability to interpret, compare, contrast, and/or create by participating in discussions, preparing reports, or completing special projects.

*Skill level:*

Application; analysis; synthesis; evaluation

*Description:*

Students choose from an array of suggested follow-up activities which will help them process the story and respond creatively to the story's conflicts and themes. The activities encourage students of varying abilities to employ higher-level thinking skills.

*continued*

# AENEAS' TRIP TO THE UNDERWORLD

*Suggestion:*

You may wish to use this page as a teacher reference and assign projects to individuals or groups. However, the page also may be reproduced so that students can select their own topics.

Although the suggested activities are divided into categories such as **Class discussion** and **Written or oral reports**, most of the topics can be adapted for use in many ways.

## SPOTLIGHT ON VOCABULARY

Study the words and meanings shown in the box.
Then complete each sentence below by writing the
correct word on the line.

---

**assured**—freed from doubt
**collapsed**—fell down or apart
**condemned**—wrongdoers; those
    judged guilty of crimes
**descendants**—offspring; children,
    great-grandchildren, etc.
**desperately**—in a wild, almost
    hopeless, way

**destiny**—one's future or fate
**endured**—put up with
**fork**—a split or division
**predict**—to say what the future will
    be; foretell
**selflessness**—unselfishness;
    generosity

---

1.  Todd _____ pain and hunger when he was lost in the
    woods for three days.

2.  With _____, Marty volunteered to teach the young boy
    how to read better.

3.  Before the game, the coach asked the team to _____
    the final score.

4.  Miriam believes it is her _____ to become a star.

5.  At the _____ in the road, Casey had to decide which
    path would lead him home.

6.  In a panic, Terri cried _____ for help after her father
    fell down the stairs and broke his leg.

7.  Titus feared he'd fail the math test, but I knew he could pass it, so
    I _____ him.

8.  Deon felt faint and then _____ on the floor.

9.  After they were judged guilty, the _____ were taken
    away to prison.

10. Aunt Marlis, the oldest woman in the family, made quilts for all of her
    known _____.

Name _____

## SETTING THE STAGE

These questions will help you get ready to read "Aeneas' Trip to the Underworld." Prepare to discuss the questions by jotting down answers on the lines.

1. The main character of this story, Aeneas, has left his homeland to search for a new one. For seven years he wanders, unable to find a new home. Imagine what it might be like to be homeless and searching for a home. Then answer these questions.

   a. How would you go about finding a new home? _____

   _____

   _____

   _____

   b. What hardships do you think you would suffer? _____

   _____

   _____

   _____

   c. What might you learn from this situation? _____

   _____

   _____

   _____

*continued*

2. In this story, Aeneas visits the Underworld and speaks to his father's ghost. Suppose you could speak to someone who has died. Now answer these questions.

a. Whom would you want to talk with? Why? _____

_____

_____

_____

b. What would you ask this person? _____

_____

_____

_____

c. How do you think this person will respond to your questions? Why? _____

_____

_____

_____

RETOLD CLASSIC MYTHS, VOL. 1

Copyright 1990. Perfection Learning Corporation, Logan, Iowa 51546

## IT HAPPENED LIKE THIS

Write the letter of the best answer on the line.

_____ 1. Aeneas and his people left Troy
after
a. Pluto set fire to the city.
b. Aeneas had a vision that told
him to find a new home.
c. Anchises learned that the
Greeks planned to attack.

_____ 2. Anchises' ghost tells Aeneas to
a. return to Troy.
b. sail on to Jupiter's kingdom.
c. find the Sibyl.

_____ 3. Before Aeneas can enter the
Underworld, he must find
a. a hidden golden bough.
b. Pluto's queen.
c. the Sibyl's magic wand.

_____ 4. Just inside the Gates of Hades,
Aeneas sees
a. all the evils of the world.
b. his dead father.
c. Pluto's lovely wife.

_____ 5. Palinurus begs Aeneas to find
his body and bury it because
a. he can't enter the Underworld
without a burial.
b. the Sibyl will then restore
Palinurus to life.
c. his wife will not rest until this
is done.

_____ 6. Charon allows Aeneas on his
boat only when
a. Aeneas draws a sword.
b. the Sibyl orders him to do so.
c. Aeneas shows him the bough.

_____ 7. Aeneas sees Dido in the Underworld and
a. begs her to forgive him for
leaving her.
b. ignores her because she left
him.
c. tries to make her return to
earth with him.

_____ 8. The Elysian Fields differ from
the rest of the Underworld
because
a. people are punished there.
b. it is beautiful and peaceful.
c. the sun doesn't shine there.

_____ 9. Aeneas tries to hug his father
and can't because
a. the Sibyl forbids it.
b. Anchises is a ghost.
c. his father flees.

_____ 10. Anchises gives Aeneas hope
when he says Aeneas will
a. start a great new race on
earth.
b. find his beloved wife again.
c. be led back home to Troy.

## VOCABULARY REVIEW

These sentences are taken from the story. Circle the
answer that comes closest in meaning to each word in
**dark type.**

1. "His nightmare had recaptured all the evils he had **endured** in the
   past years."
       a. caused      b. suffered      c. destroyed

2. " 'Once you are in Italy, seek out the Sibyl, who can **predict** the
   future.' "
       a. prevent      b. change      c. foretell

3. " 'You lead the Trojans with **selflessness**, good faith, and
   wisdom.' "
       a. generosity      b. peace      c. bravery

4. " 'I ask for no more than my **destiny**,' replied Aeneas."
       a. fate      b. share      c. rights

5. "Palinurus **desperately** begged, 'Then find my body, dear prince!
   Throw handfuls of dirt on it so that my spirit may have rest!' "
       a. angrily      b. wildly      c. sadly

6. "The Sibyl **assured** him. 'Do not fear us. We are not here to make
   mischief.' "
       a. lied to      b. freed from      c. gave in to
                                 doubt

7. "The greedy Cerberus swallowed the cake. Then almost immediately
   the huge dog **collapsed**."
       a. fell down      b. went mad      c. grew angry

8. "The Sibyl guided him onward until they reached a **fork** in the
   road. There they stopped."
       a. bump      b. bridge      c. division

9. " 'To the right are the Elysian Fields where you will find your
   father,' the Sibyl answered. 'To the left are the **condemned**.' "
       a. dying      b. guilty      c. poor

10. "Here, he pointed out Aeneas' future son, grandson, and other
    **descendants**."
        a. neighbors      b. losers      c. offspring

RETOLD CLASSIC MYTHS, VOL. 1

# AENEAS' TRIP TO THE UNDERWORLD

## LITERARY FOCUS: PLOT DEVICES

The *plot* is the sequence of events in a story. Usually in a story, a character meets up with obstacles or difficulties. Then he or she tries to overcome them. These struggles are called *conflicts*.

Sometimes a character is able to overcome a difficulty through inner strength. But often a character needs outside help. Such help may come in the form of an object, person, or animal. It could even be a vision, ritual, or magical spell. These aids—or *plot devices*—help the character overcome the difficulty and also help advance the story.

In this myth, a number of plot devices are used to move along the story. Play the game and take Aeneas through nine obstacles he faces in the myth. Fill out the gameboard by describing either the plot device or what occurs after the device is used (plot advance).

Good luck! The first one is done for you.

*continued*

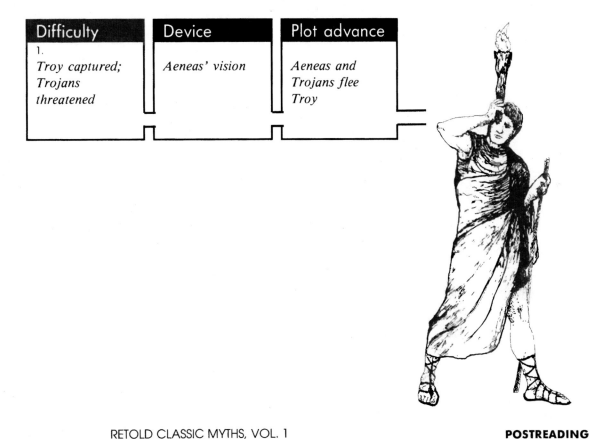

| Difficulty | Device | Plot advance |
|---|---|---|
| 1. *Troy captured; Trojans threatened* | *Aeneas' vision* | *Aeneas and Trojans flee Troy* |

81

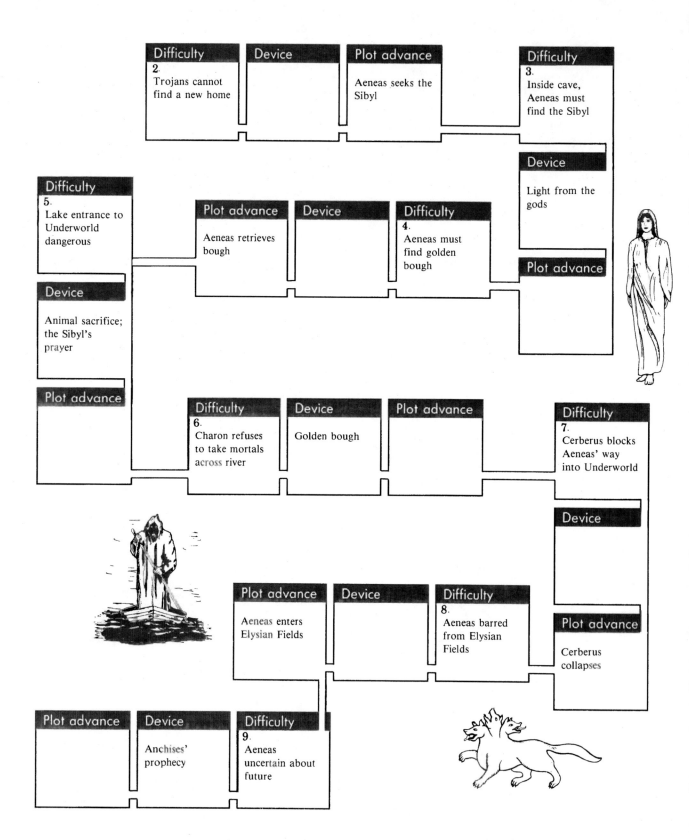

**Difficulty**

2.
Trojans cannot
find a new home

**Device**

**Plot advance**

Aeneas seeks the
Sibyl

**Difficulty**

3.
Inside cave,
Aeneas must
find the Sibyl

**Device**

Light from the
gods

**Plot advance**

**Difficulty**

5.
Lake entrance to
Underworld
dangerous

**Plot advance**

Aeneas retrieves
bough

**Device**

**Difficulty**

4.
Aeneas must
find golden
bough

**Device**

Animal sacrifice;
the Sibyl's
prayer

**Plot advance**

**Difficulty**

6.
Charon refuses
to take mortals
across river

**Device**

Golden bough

**Plot advance**

**Difficulty**

7.
Cerberus blocks
Aeneas' way
into Underworld

**Device**

**Plot advance**

Cerberus
collapses

**Plot advance**

Aeneas enters
Elysian Fields

**Device**

**Difficulty**

8.
Aeneas barred
from Elysian
Fields

**Plot advance**

**Device**

Anchises'
prophecy

**Difficulty**

9.
Aeneas
uncertain about
future

Name _____

## THE READING-WRITING CONNECTION: UNLOCKING PASSAGES

Answer the questions about these quotes taken from "Aeneas' Trip to the Underworld." (Go back to the story if you need more clues.) Write your response to part *c* of each question on a separate sheet of paper.

1. "In the silence of the night, Aeneas prayed. Maybe the gods could help him find a new home for the future Trojan children." (page 74)

   a. What does the passage mean as used in the story?

   _____

   _____

   b. Why is Aeneas searching for a new home?

   _____

   _____

   _____

   _____

   c. **Journal writing:** Describe a time when you asked for help. Did you receive help? If so, tell how. If not, tell what happened instead.

2. " 'Goddess of the Underworld! You who watch over the souls of the dead! Open the gates to your mysterious domain deep in the earth! . . . And by your will, we shall move among the ghosts. We shall see what secrets are buried from the World of Light.' " (page 77)

   a. What does the passage mean as used in the story?

   _____

   _____

*continued*

b. What is the World of Light? What secrets are hidden from it?

_____

_____

_____

_____

c. **Journal writing:** Describe a hidden world you would like to visit.
What secrets might you find hidden there?

3.   "The Sibyl spoke again but in a softer voice. 'Your time will soon
     come, Palinurus. Your body will be found by a coastal people. And
     they will give you a proper funeral.' " (page 79)

a. What does the passage mean as used in the story?

_____

_____

b. What emotion do you think Palinurus feels when the Sibyl reveals
the future? Why?

_____

_____

_____

_____

c. **Journal writing:** Describe a time when you desperately wanted
something. What did you want? Did your wish come true? Explain.

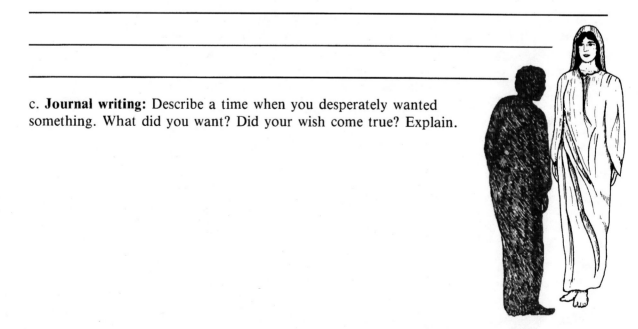

RETOLD CLASSIC MYTHS, VOL. 1

## WRITING CORNER: CREATING A WORLD

Writers sometimes dream up new worlds to entertain their readers. This
is especially true in myths, science fiction, or fantasy stories. To create a
new world, writers must imagine new types of settings and characters.
They will also give a mood to their new world.

Suppose you want to write a story that takes place in a new world.
The following activity will help you create such a place. It could be an
underworld, a new planet, or a secret place on earth. You decide. Then
answer the questions.

1.  How will your world look, feel, sound, and smell? Will it be light
    or dark, hot or cold? Will it be colorful, rocky, perhaps slimy?
    Will your world be full of sound or silent?

    List the words here that describe your planet:

    _____

    _____

    _____

    _____

2.  Who lives in your new world? Are your characters like people or
    animals on earth? Or are they strange? Do they talk, walk, or
    eat? What do they wear? What are their personalities like?

    Describe the characters of your world here:

    _____

    _____

    _____

    _____

    _____

    _____

*continued*

3. What happens in your world? Describe the usual activities. For example, is there farming? Are there businesses or factories? What do the adults do? What do the children do?
   Describe the activities in your world here:

   _____

   _____

   _____

   _____

   _____

   _____

   _____

4. Finally, what is the mood of your world? Is it a happy place? Or is it creepy? Is it a place where you would like to live?
   Describe the mood of your world here:

   _____

   _____

   _____

   _____

5. Now put it all together. Write a complete description of your new world on another sheet of paper. Take details from your notes and use them to describe the setting, characters, activities, and mood of your world. Give your description a title. Then share it with a friend or the whole class.

## ONE STEP FURTHER

### Class discussion

1. Aeneas has a vision that tells him to flee Troy and find a new home. So he and his people leave Troy in search of one. Why do you think Aeneas trusts his vision? If someone you know had a vision, would you encourage him or her to follow it? Explain your response.

2. Anchises and the Sibyl both predict the future. Do you think their predictions for Aeneas will come true? Why or why not? Have any of their other predictions come true? If so, which ones?

3. Both Aeneas and Palinurus have painful memories of the storm at sea. Why does each feel guilty? Are either of them to blame for the tragedy? Why or why not?

4. Who are some of the condemned in the Underworld? Tell why they are being punished. Then describe their punishment. Do you believe they are being treated justly or unjustly? Explain your opinion.

5. Aeneas is both a warrior and a hero. Yet he can't bear to hear babies cry. And when Dido ignores him, Aeneas cries. Does Aeneas fit your idea of a hero? Do his actions make him more or less of a hero? Explain.

### Written or oral reports

1. What kind of place is the Underworld? Find descriptions of it throughout the story. You may also use other sources from your library to aid you. Then put these details together, and make a report about the setting of the Underworld. You may wish to draw a map to go along with your report.

2. A number of characters from mythology appear during Aeneas' trip. In a mythology book, look up several of these characters who interest you. Then write a description of each

of these characters. You may want to discuss their personalities and actions. Also, if you find pictures of these characters, you might include them in your report as well.

3. Pluto and Proserpina are king and queen of the Underworld. How did each become a ruler in the Underworld? Are their stories happy ones? Give your opinion along with your report on how they came to be rulers.

4. Find out how Aeneas finally gained his new homeland. You will find his story in a mythology book. How does this story figure in the early history of Italy? Look up the actual history in a history book. Then answer these questions, too: How do the two accounts compare? How are they different? Report your findings to the class.

### Creative writing activities

1. Read the story of Dido and Aeneas. Then write a letter from Aeneas to Dido. In the letter, explain why you had to leave her. Also, tell her what your feelings are for her now.

2. Imagine that you are one of the Trojans on Aeneas' ship. Aeneas has just returned from the Underworld. In a diary entry, describe your thoughts and reactions to his return and his good news.

3. Write a poem or song about Aeneas' trip to the Underworld.

4. Imagine you are a charity worker. Design a plea for Aeneas and the Trojans to help them find a new home. Write the plea to convince some ruler to let the Trojans live in his or her country.

5. Suppose you are the Sibyl. Write a magazine article in which you discuss why you took Aeneas to the Underworld.

*continued*

## Artistic activities

1. Make a comic strip of an adventure from the story. You might choose Aeneas finding the golden bough or the Sibyl and Aeneas sacrificing the cows. Or you could show Aeneas meeting Charon or Cerberus. Be sure to describe what is happening in each frame of the strip.

2. Aeneas sees "ghostly evils" in front of the Gates of Hades. They are Disease, Old Age, Grief, Fear, Starvation, Death, Pain, and War. Use your imagination to draw or paint one or more of these evils.

3. Create a collage which contrasts the Elysian Fields with another part of the Underworld. Use images which show the different moods found in each part.

## Small-group activities

1. Take a poll of your class. Ask them, "Is it possible to predict the future?" Ask each person to give examples that support his or her opinion.

2. Choose a scene from Aeneas' trip and turn it into a short play or video show. First write out the dialogue and stage directions, and describe the sound effects you will use. Then practice the show. Finally, tape or present your scene to the class.

# THE FOLLIES OF MIDAS

## PREREADING ACTIVITIES

### Story Themes
Several themes of "The Follies of Midas" are listed below. They will help you prepare activities which will stimulate students' interest and involvement in the story.

1.) Hasty decisions often lead to trouble.
2.) Greed can cloud good judgment.
3.) It is best to stay in favor with those who are more powerful.
4.) A person may suffer from his or her mistakes, even while learning from them.
5.) People get what they deserve.

### Spotlight on Vocabulary
### [Guided Practice]
*Objective:*
The learner will demonstrate an understanding of ten vocabulary words by showing which word belongs in each of ten sentences.

*Skill level:*
Knowledge/recall; application

*Description:*
This exercise introduces students to ten words in the story which may be new to them. First students preview the words and their definitions. Then they use the words to complete ten sentences.

The sentences discuss topics familiar to most students, so they can see how the new words fit into their existing web of knowledge. The goal of the exercise is to help students read the story more easily. Complete mastery of the vocabulary words at this stage is not expected.

*Suggestion:*
If prereading vocabulary work is kept short, word study can build interest without dampening enthusiasm. Exposure to these ten selected words will give students a head start toward understanding the story. A *postreading* vocabulary check and suggestions for further vocabulary study are provided for use *after* students have read the story.

### Setting the Stage
### [Anticipatory Set]
*Objective:*
The learner will demonstrate an understanding of the results of hasty decisions by analyzing such a decision and its consequences. The learner will then show an understanding of the lessons learned from mistakes by evaluating a personal experience.

*Skill level:*
Analysis; synthesis; evaluation

*Description:*
In part 1, students are asked to think about a hasty decision they made and later regretted. Then they answer questions about that decision and make suggestions about how they might avoid hasty decisions in the future.

In part 2, students think about a mistake they made from which they learned a lesson. On a graphic organizer, students explain the mistake and write one bad and one good consequence resulting from the mistake. Last they show the lesson they learned.

*Suggestion:*
Ask students to think of examples of decisions made in literature, movies, or history. Help them analyze the decisions to decide if any could be viewed as mistakes. Then have students determine how a different decision may have changed the outcome of the book, movie, or historical event.

## THE FOLLIES OF MIDAS

# POSTREADING ACTIVITIES

### It Happened Like This
### [Check for Understanding]

*Objective:*

The learner will demonstrate comprehension of the story by correctly answering ten multiple-choice questions.

*Skill level:*

Knowledge; comprehension

*Description:*

This exercise tests recall of important facts in the story. Students identify, from three choices, the answer that correctly completes each of ten sentences.

*Suggestion:*

Page number references on the response key show where the answer to each question can be found. These page numbers can be given to students who are taking an open-book test. The page numbers are also helpful when discussing the quiz after papers have been corrected.

### Vocabulary Review
### [Check for Understanding]

*Objective:*

The learner will demonstrate an understanding of ten words by identifying the correct synonym for each.

*Skill level:*

Knowledge

*Description:*

This exercise tests mastery of the ten words introduced in the **Spotlight on Vocabulary** exercise. The words are presented in the context of sentences taken directly from the story. Students identify, from three choices, the correct synonym for each word.

*Suggestion:*

Results of the vocabulary check will show which words students find most difficult. You may wish to provide further reinforcement for problem words.

### Literary Focus: Humor
### [Guided or Independent Practice]

*Objective:*

The learner will demonstrate an understanding of comic devices by identifying such devices used in the myth.

*Skill level:*

Analysis; evaluation

*Description:*

First the student is given definitions of the comic devices of hyperbole, understatement, irony, and sarcasm. Then ten quotations from the story are presented. For each example, the student is to analyze the quotation and indicate which of the four comic devices it employs.

*Suggestion:*

Ask students to identify examples of these comic devices in their own speech and writing. Discuss which types are most effective in different kinds of writing. Students might also enjoy taking an idea and inventing four examples of dialogue, each using a different comic device, to communicate this idea.

### The Reading-Writing Connection:
### Unlocking Passages
### [Guided or Independent Practice]

*Objective:*

The learner will demonstrate an ability to make inferences by answering questions based on quotations from the story.

*Skill level:*

Comprehension; application; analysis

*Description:*

First students read a quotation; then they answer three questions about the quote.

*continued*

# THE FOLLIES OF MIDAS

The first question requires an interpretation of the quote. The second question requires an inference. The third question, to be answered in a journal entry, asks students to relate the quotation to their personal experience or views.

The questions are intended to lead students to greater understanding and appreciation of the story. The questions also allow students to bridge the gap between their own knowledge and story concepts.

Quotation 1 concerns Bacchus' astonishment at the greed of Midas. Quotation 2 concerns Midas' realization that riches are not all there is to happiness. Quotation 3 concerns the statement that people must learn through their own mistakes and experiences.

*Suggestion:*

Make the questions the subject of small-group or class discussion.

## Writing Corner: Make a Wish
## [Extending Students' Thinking]

*Objective:*

The learner will demonstrate an understanding of the decision-making process by identifying some personal wishes, analyzing them for benefits and drawbacks, and then using this analysis to make a decision.

*Skill level:*

Analysis; synthesis; evaluation

*Description:*

First students fill in a table by listing five wishes they might consider making if they were in Midas' place. Then they are asked to identify and record the possible benefits and drawbacks of each wish. Using this information, they are to rank the wishes and select their top wish. Finally, students write a speech to Bacchus telling him about the wishes they considered and convincing him that their top choice is the best one.

*Suggestion:*

Have students present their top wishes to the members of the class. Then have each student choose another's wish and write a story telling what happens when Bacchus grants the wish. Have the author of each story share the story with the person who made the wish.

## One Step Further
## [Extending Students' Thinking]

*Objective:*

The learner will demonstrate an ability to interpret, compare, contrast, and/or create by participating in discussions, preparing reports, or completing special projects.

*Skill level:*

Application; analysis; synthesis; evaluation

*Description:*

Students choose from an array of suggested follow-up activities which will help them process the story and respond creatively to the story's conflicts and themes. The activities encourage students of varying abilities to employ higher-level thinking skills.

*Suggestion:*

You may wish to use this page as a teacher reference and assign projects to individuals or groups. However, the page also may be reproduced so that students can select their own topics.

Although the suggested activities are divided into categories such as **Class discussion** and **Written or oral reports**, most of the topics can be adapted for use in many ways.

## SPOTLIGHT ON VOCABULARY

Study the words and meanings in the box. Then complete each sentence below by writing the correct word on the line.

| | |
|---|---|
| **confiding**—telling in secret | **nudged**—pushed or elbowed |
| **deliriously**—wildly; madly | **procession**—moving line of people |
| **enraptured**—delighted; thrilled | or things; parade |
| **gracious**—kind; polite | **renounce**—give up |
| **inadequate**—unsatisfactory; | **tutor**—private teacher |
| not enough | **verdict**—decision; judgment |

1. The _____ of circus animals and clowns marched around the arena before the show began.

2. Travis got behind in French class, so he hired (a, an) _____ to teach him privately.

3. Lance regretted _____ his fears to Gloria; he worried she might tell his secrets.

4. Anyone who has quit smoking knows that it is not easy to _____ the habit.

5. After several hours, the jury reached a decision and announced a guilty _____.

6. The overjoyed author danced _____ in the street when she learned her book would be published.

7. Luis was _____ by the beautiful symphony and sat listening to it hour after hour.

8. Joyce looked at her skimpy, _____ notes and realized she did not have enough information to study for the test.

9. To get my attention, Sam gently _____ me in the side.

10. The _____ hostess warmly welcomed us to her house for dinner.

## SETTING THE STAGE

These questions will help you get ready to read "The Follies of Midas." Prepare to discuss the questions by jotting down answers on the lines.

1. King Midas does not always think before he makes a decision. So he must live with some unhappy results. Think about a time when you made a hasty decision that you later regretted.

   a. Briefly explain your quick decision. _____

   _____

   _____

   _____

   b. Why did you later regret your decision? _____

   _____

   _____

   _____

   c. What might help you from making such hasty decisions in the future? _____

   _____

   _____

   _____

*continued*

2. In this myth, King Midas makes mistakes. He seems to learn from these mistakes, but he suffers for them. Think about some mistakes you have made that taught you a lesson. Write one on the diagram. Then list a good result and a bad result from having made that mistake. Finally, write the lesson you learned from this experience.

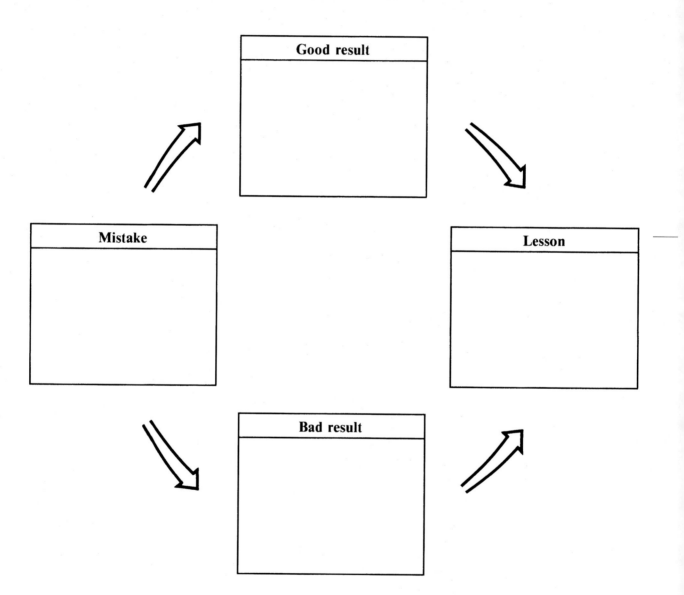

RETOLD CLASSIC MYTHS, VOL. 1
Copyright 1990. Perfection Learning Corporation, Logan, Iowa 51546

Name _____

## IT HAPPENED LIKE THIS

Write the letter of the best answer on the line.

_____ 1. The "beggar" Midas' servants bring to the palace is
a. Pan's helper.
b. Bacchus' tutor.
c. Midas' gardener.

_____ 2. Bacchus rewards Midas for
a. selecting Pan's music.
b. giving up wine.
c. returning Silenus.

_____ 3. Midas' wish causes trouble because Midas cannot
a. eat and drink.
b. sleep at night.
c. make everyone happy.

_____ 4. Midas' wish is removed when he
a. washes under the River Pactolus' waterfall.
b. promises not to be greedy anymore.
c. apologizes to Silenus.

_____ 5. Midas learns all *but which* of the following from his wish:
a. to think before he speaks.
b. to share his wealth.
c. to appreciate the simple pleasures.

_____ 6. Pan and Apollo ask Midas to judge their
a. voices.
b. music.
c. originality.

_____ 7. Apollo says he is giving Midas the ears of an ass because Midas'
a. manners are like an animal.
b. voice already sounds like an ass'.
c. ears are too small to hear well.

_____ 8. At first, the only one who knows about Midas' plight is his
a. barber.
b. cook.
c. tailor.

_____ 9. Midas' secret becomes known after
a. the reeds and wind spread the gossip.
b. he is seen bathing in the River Pactolus.
c. Apollo reveals the truth at one of Midas' feasts.

_____ 10. Midas' neighbors feel his appearance is deserved because he
a. never listened to anybody.
b. always horsed around with his servants.
c. looks like the ass he is.

RETOLD CLASSIC MYTHS, VOL. 1

## VOCABULARY REVIEW

These sentences are taken from the story. Circle the
answer that comes closest in meaning to each word in
**dark type**.

1. "The tallest of the men **nudged** the smallest. 'Wake him up!'
   The smaller replied with a stronger nudge. 'You wake him!'"
   - a. begged
   - b. ordered
   - c. elbowed

2. "As this small **procession** moved down the road, peasants in the
   fields stared."
   - a. carriage
   - b. parade
   - c. herd

3. "'The gentleman before you is Silenus. He is . . . **tutor** of Bacchus.'"
   - a. private teacher
   - b. old friend
   - c. fierce defender

4. "'Bacchus, you are far too **gracious**. But if you insist. . .'"
   - a. kind
   - b. tricky
   - c. wise

5. "A wiser man might have paused at those words. Not Midas. He
   went off **deliriously** happy."
   - a. oddly
   - b. wildly
   - c. privately

6. "'. . . if you would like to **renounce** your wish, I can help you.'"
   - a. give up
   - b. ask again
   - c. return with

7. "Suddenly a few sweet notes of music drifted to him. Midas was
   **enraptured**."
   - a. puzzled
   - b. delighted
   - c. jealous

8. "Satisfied, Apollo turned to Midas. 'Well, Midas? Your **verdict**?'"
   - a. secret
   - b. idea
   - c. decision

9. "'But I should have guessed that with those ears, you might not be
   the best judge. Such tiny, **inadequate** ears.'"
   - a. unsuitable
   - b. unhearing
   - c. delicate

10. "After **confiding** the secret, the barber felt better at once."
    - a. telling
    - b. reviewing
    - c. discovering

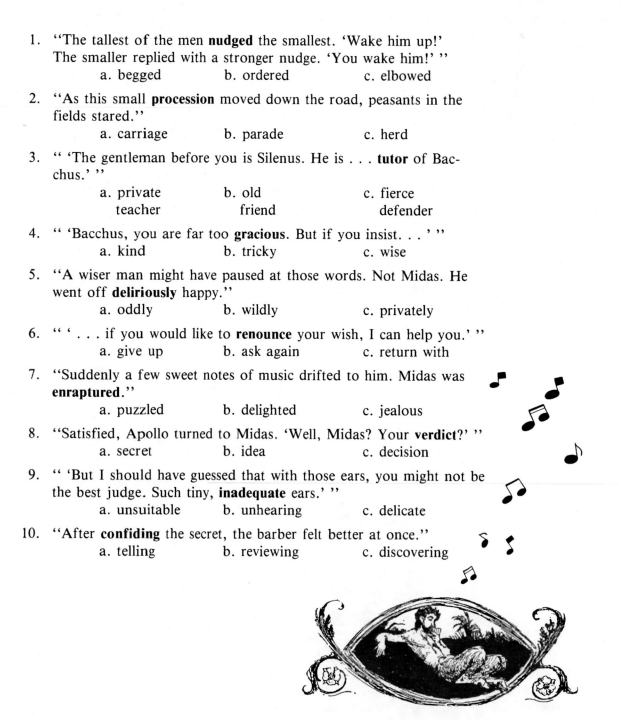

RETOLD CLASSIC MYTHS, VOL. 1

Copyright 1990. Perfection Learning Corporation, Logan, Iowa 51546

## LITERARY FOCUS: HUMOR

The myth of Midas contains comic elements. In this retelling of the myth, humor is created through a number of devices. These are explained below.

*Hyperbole:* a wild exaggeration or overstatement. "Our new basketball player wears a flashing light to warn off low-flying planes" is hyperbole.

*Understatement:* a comment that downplays or undervalues something. "Cory's little streak of luck began when he won three million dollars in the lottery."

*Irony:* a contrast between what is said and what is meant or what results. " 'I trust Tony completely,' said Maria just two days before he robbed her."

*Sarcasm:* a bitter or sneering remark made to mock a person, thing, or idea. Sarcasm is more obvious than irony. "With friends like you, who needs enemies?" is a sarcastic statement.

Now read the following quotes from "The Follies of Midas" and decide which type of humorous device is being used. Write

> *H* for hyperbole,
>
> *U* for understatement,
>
> *I* for irony, and
>
> *S* for sarcasm.

Some quotes may contain more than one device, but you need only identify one. Be prepared to give reasons for your decisions.

_____ 1.  " 'I'll sing and romp the way I like / Until the moon's gone blue!' "

_____ 2.  " 'Yes, I said Bacchus. It seems even you fools know the god of wine and revelry.' "

_____ 3.  "All that drinking made them a little lively. By the end of the first day, every plate in the palace had been broken."

*continued*

_____ 4. " 'What do you have on the back of that ass?' one peasant shouted. The taller servant yelled back, 'Your wife, dear sir! Picked her up on the road this morning! A hairy little thing, ain't she?' As you might imagine, the peasant found the joke mildly insulting. He chased the servants with a shower of well-aimed rocks.' "

_____ 5. "Apollo laughed. 'Now you have ears fit for a king. The King of Fools, that is.' "

_____ 6. "Relief rushed over Midas. 'Great Bacchus, thank you. I'll never be so stupid again.' "

_____ 7. " 'At last Midas looks like the ass he always was.' "

_____ 8. [Upon discovering Silenus, one of the servants commented,] 'He smells like a wine cellar!' "

_____ 9. " 'Very well, Midas. Your wish is granted. But in the future, I hope you pick your wishes more carefully,' [Bacchus said.]"

## THE READING-WRITING CONNECTION: UNLOCKING PASSAGES

Answer the questions about these quotes taken from
"The Follies of Midas." (Go back to the story if you
need more clues.) Write your response to part *c* of
each question on a separate sheet of paper.

1. "Bacchus could scarcely believe such a greedy request. Midas was
   already the richest ruler in the land. Now he wanted more."
   (page 93)

   a. What does the passage mean as used in the story?

   _____

   _____

   b. Midas is already wealthy. Why do you think he wants more
   riches?

   _____

   _____

   _____

   _____

   c. **Journal writing:** What should a rich person do with his or her
   wealth? Write your opinions in a journal entry.

2. " 'What good is gold if I can't eat or drink?' Midas com-
   plained. . . . 'I'd rather be a poor man with a full belly.' "
   (page 95)

   a. What does the passage mean as used in the story?

   _____

   _____

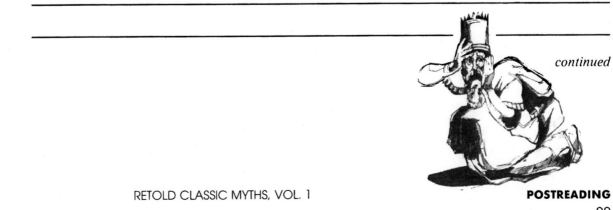

*continued*

b. What does Midas learn about what's most important in life?

_____

_____

_____

_____

c. **Journal writing:** Write about a time when what you thought was important turned out not to be so. What became more important to you as a result of this experience?

3. " ' . . . the hard lessons must be experienced, not taught. They are for each of us to learn alone.' " (page 95)

a. What does the passage mean as used in the story?

_____

_____

b. Why does Bacchus believe that "the hard lessons must be experienced"?

_____

_____

_____

_____

c. **Journal writing:** Do you believe that hard lessons have to be experienced? Why or why not?

## WRITING CORNER: MAKE A WISH

Suppose you are in Midas' place. Bacchus has just offered you a reward. However, this time, you decide to carefully consider your decision before making your wish.

To help organize your thoughts, fill in the wish table below. First, list your wishes. Next, list likely benefits if that wish came true. Then identify likely drawbacks that might occur. Finally, weigh all the benefits and drawbacks. Rate your wishes from 1 to 5, with 1 being your top wish.

| Ranking | Wish Table |
|---|---|
| _____ | Wish _____ |
| | Likely Benefits _____ |
| | _____ |
| | _____ |
| | Likely Drawbacks _____ |
| | _____ |
| | _____ |
| _____ | Wish _____ |
| | Likely Benefits _____ |
| | _____ |
| | Likely Drawbacks _____ |
| | _____ |
| | _____ |

*continued*

| Ranking | Wish Table |
|---|---|
| _____ | Wish _____ |
| | Likely Benefits _____ |
| | _____ |
| | _____ |
| | Likely Drawbacks _____ |
| | _____ |
| | _____ |
| _____ | Wish _____ |
| | Likely Benefits _____ |
| | _____ |
| | _____ |
| | Likely Drawbacks _____ |
| | _____ |
| | _____ |
| _____ | Wish _____ |
| | Likely Benefits _____ |
| | _____ |
| | _____ |
| | Likely Drawbacks _____ |
| | _____ |
| | _____ |

Now on another sheet of paper, write a speech to Bacchus in which you state your decision. Tell him what wishes you considered. Also explain why you finally picked one as your top wish. Your goal should be to convince him that you thoroughly considered the benefits and drawbacks of your wishes.

## ONE STEP FURTHER

### Class discussion

1. Do you think Midas' chief fault is stupidity? Or does he get into trouble for other reasons? Explain your point of view and give evidence from the story to back up your opinion.

2. If you were asked to sum up the moral of the story in a single sentence, what would you say? Do you think that moral is still important for people today? Give examples to support your opinion.

3. What might happen to Midas after the story ends? Is he likely to get rid of his ass' ears? Do you think his behavior will change? Use evidence from the story to help you make your prediction.

4. Which of the gods or mythical creatures in the story is the most appealing to you? Which one seems most threatening? What is Midas' attitude toward these creatures and gods?

### Written or oral reports

1. Have your librarian help you find information about satyrs. What is their origin? What role did they play in Greek mythology? Be prepared to share your findings with your classmates.

2. Find a copy of the children's book *The Chocolate Touch* by Patrick S. Cling. Read the book and report to your class how the book is similar to and different from "The Follies of Midas." You may also wish to tell the story of the chocolate touch to a class of young children.

3. Watch the video of the James Bond adventure *Goldfinger*. How is the Midas myth used in this movie? Review the video for your class and include comments on the connection between the myth and the movie.

4. Research ancient Greek music. What instruments were played and what kind of songs were sung? What role did the Greeks imagine for Pan and Apollo in the development of music? Report to your classmates on your findings.

### Creative writing activities

1. Review Silenus' two songs at the beginning of the story. Then write some songs for other parts of the story. For example, try writing a song that Midas and Silenus might have sung as they drank and feasted. You could also write a song that Midas might have sung when he first used his "golden touch."

2. Suppose you attended Midas' celebration dinner. Write a letter to a friend who could not attend. Tell him or her about the dinner and how you reacted to Midas' golden touch. Also explain your feelings when Midas suddenly left before the meal was over.

3. Suppose this statement appeared at the end of Midas' tale: " . . . he hadn't been cured of stupidity. So Midas soon found himself in trouble again." Write another scene in which Midas' stupidity causes him trouble again.

*continued*

## Artistic activities

1. Imagine that you are the producer for a ballet entitled *Midas*. Create two dances for the ballet. Also try to find appropriate music for the dances. Then design or find pictures of costumes that could be used in your ballet.

2. Design or build a trophy to give to the winner of the gods' music contest. You might also design one to give to the runner-up.

3. Use gold paint or gold foil to make a miniature stage set for the play *Midas' Golden Touch*.

## Small-group activities

1. Have your group find out what is the current meaning of the phrase *Midas touch*. If a person has this touch, is he or she thought to be lucky or unlucky? Why? How does this compare to Midas' experience? After this discussion, make a list of the pros and cons of having the Midas touch (in the current sense). Be prepared to share your group's conclusions with the others in the class.

2. The mood (overall feeling) in this story varies. For example, in the beginning, the mood is lighthearted. But it becomes more serious several pages later. Identify other moods in the myth. Then find music and pictures to capture these moods. Finally, write a script or use selections from the story to present your audiovisual version of "The Follies of Midas."

## CUPID AND PSYCHE

# PREREADING ACTIVITIES

### Story Themes

Several themes of "Cupid and Psyche" are listed below. They will help you prepare activities which will stimulate students' interest and involvement in the story.

1.) People should not be judged by appearances.
2.) Love can come unexpectedly.
3.) Trust is necessary to a relationship.
4.) Letting others influence your personal decisions can be a mistake.
5.) Love is a powerful force.

### Spotlight on Vocabulary
### [Guided Practice]

*Objective:*

The learner will demonstrate an understanding of ten vocabulary words by showing which word belongs in each of ten sentences.

*Skill level:*

Knowledge/recall; application

*Description:*

This exercise introduces students to ten words in the story which may be new to them. First students preview the words and their definitions. Then they use the words to complete ten sentences.

The sentences discuss topics familiar to most students, so they can see how the new words fit into their existing web of knowledge. The goal of the exercise is to help students read the story more easily. Complete mastery of the vocabulary words at this stage is not expected.

*Suggestion:*

If prereading vocabulary work is kept short, word study can build interest without dampening enthusiasm. Exposure to these ten selected words will give students a head start toward understanding the story. A *postreading* vocabulary check and suggestions for further vocabulary study are provided for use *after* students have read the story.

### Setting the Stage
### [Anticipatory Set]

*Objective:*

The learner will analyze and suggest solutions to four obstacles to love. The learner will also define love, examine behavior it may lead to, and interpret some common sayings about love.

*Skill level:*

Analysis; synthesis; evaluation

*Description:*

In part 1, students suggest a possible solution to four common obstacles to love. Then they compare their solutions with others to decide which might be most useful.

In part 2, students write a personal definition of love. Then they write about how those in love may act differently than others. Next students decide if some common sayings about love are true or false, giving reasons for their views. Students may also use other common sayings they know.

*Suggestion:*

Ask students to reexamine the obstacles. Have them identify lovers from history or literature who faced some of the obstacles listed. Then ask them how the lovers solved or failed to solve the obstacles.

## CUPID AND PSYCHE

# POSTREADING ACTIVITIES

## It Happened Like This
### [Check for Understanding]

*Objective:*

The learner will demonstrate comprehension of the story by correctly answering ten multiple-choice questions.

*Skill level:*

Knowledge; comprehension

*Description:*

This exercise tests recall of important facts in the story. Students identify, from three choices, the answer that correctly completes each of ten sentences.

*Suggestion:*

Page number references on the response key show where the answer to each question can be found. These page numbers can be given to students who are taking an open-book test. The page numbers are also helpful when discussing the quiz after papers have been corrected.

## Vocabulary Review
### [Check for Understanding]

*Objective:*

The learner will demonstrate an understanding of ten words by identifying the correct synonym for each.

*Skill level:*

Knowledge

*Description:*

This exercise tests mastery of the ten words introduced in the **Spotlight on Vocabulary** exercise. The words are presented in the context of sentences taken directly from the story. Students identify, from three choices, the correct synonym for each word.

*Suggestion:*

Results of the vocabulary check will show which words students find most difficult. You may wish to provide further reinforcement for problem words.

## Literary Focus: Allegory
### [Guided or Independent Practice]

*Objective:*

The learner will demonstrate an understanding of allegory by analyzing symbols in the myth and identifying the morals or truths taught through the use of each symbol.

*Skill level:*

Analysis; evaluation

*Description:*

First the student is given a list of characters and objects which serve as symbols at the literal level of the story. The students then complete a chart by identifying the figurative meaning of each symbol and giving evidence for their decisions.

*Suggestion:*

Have students identify other examples of allegorical stories in literature. Point out that many fairy tales and folk tales are allegorical.

## The Reading-Writing Connection:
## Unlocking Passages
### [Guided or Independent Practice]

*Objective:*

The learner will demonstrate an ability to make inferences by answering questions based on quotations from the story.

*Skill level:*

Comprehension; application; analysis

*Description:*

First students read a quotation; then they answer three questions about the quote. The first question requires an interpretation of the quote. The second question requires an inference. The third question, to be answered in a journal entry, asks students to relate the quotation to their personal experience or views.

*continued*

## CUPID AND PSYCHE

The questions are intended to lead students to greater understanding and appreciation of the story. The questions also allow students to bridge the gap between their own knowledge and story concepts.

Quotation 1 concerns Cupid's feelings when he experiences love for the first time. Quotation 2 concerns Cupid and Psyche's conversation about being judged by appearances. Quotation 3 concerns Cupid's despair over Psyche's inability to love him without looking at him.

*Suggestion:*
Make the questions the subject of small-group or class discussion.

### Writing Corner: Sending a Message [Extending Students' Thinking]

*Objective:*
The learner will demonstrate an understanding of the allegory by identifying a message he or she wishes to communicate and outlining an allegorical story which will give this message.

*Skill level:*
Analysis; synthesis

*Description:*
Students study a sample outline of an allegory. Then they complete outlines of their own stories. First they identify the message they wish to communicate. Then they name the characters and settings and tell what each symbolizes. Finally, students each write a short plot outline. They are then invited to use their plot outlines to write a more detailed allegory.

*Suggestion:*
Have students share their allegorical stories. They may wish to identify stories with similar messages and compare the symbols used to get the message across.

### One Step Further [Extending Students' Thinking]

*Objective:*
The learner will demonstrate an ability to interpret, compare, contrast, and/or create by participating in discussions, preparing reports, or completing special projects.

*Skill level:*
Application; analysis; synthesis; evaluation

*Description:*
Students choose from an array of suggested follow-up activities which will help them process the story and respond creatively to the story's conflicts and themes. The activities encourage students of varying abilities to employ higher-level thinking skills.

*Suggestion:*
You may wish to use this page as a teacher reference and assign projects to individuals or groups. However, the page also may be reproduced so that students can select their own topics.

Although the suggested activities are divided into categories such as **Class discussion** and **Written or oral reports**, most of the topics can be adapted for use in many ways.

**CUPID AND PSYCHE**

## SPOTLIGHT ON VOCABULARY

Study the words and meanings shown in the box.
Then complete each sentence below by writing the
correct word on the line.

---

**bemused**—confused; puzzled
**broached**—introduced; presented
**efficiency**—ability to be quick and
    useful
**homage**—public honor or praise
**mourning**—grieving

**somber**—gloomy; dark
**stupor**—daze; trance
**throng**—crowd; mob
**ushered**—led; guided
**wavered**—trembled; flickered

---

1. The rock group was so popular that fans would _____ wherever they went.

2. The candle's flame _____ in the breeze and then went out.

3. In a public ceremony, the President gave _____ to the astronauts for their successful mission.

4. When the great leader died, many people wore black armbands to show they were _____ his death.

5. The students gave their teacher _____ looks because they did not understand her directions.

6. After hinting around for a month, Manuel finally _____ the idea of getting his own apartment to his parents.

7. A helpful servant _____ the guests to their rooms.

8. The coach wasn't usually gloomy, but his face looked _____ when his star player quit.

9. With energy and _____, Philip cleaned the house more quickly than he ever had.

10. After the battle, the young soldier was so shocked and tired that he sank into (a, an) _____ and had to be carried to camp.

Name _____

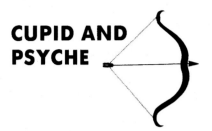

## SETTING THE STAGE

These questions will help you get ready to read "Cupid and Psyche." Prepare to discuss the questions by jotting down answers on the lines.

1. "Cupid and Psyche" is a love story. But like many lovers, Cupid and Psyche must overcome several obstacles, or difficulties, before they can be happy together.

    Read the following obstacles. How might each problem be overcome? Write your solution to each. Then compare your suggestions with your classmates' and decide which might be most useful.

    a. Obstacle: Lovers come from different backgrounds.

    Solution: _____

    _____

    _____

    _____

    b. Obstacle: Parent(s) objects to match.

    Solution: _____

    _____

    _____

    _____

    c. Obstacle: One lover distrusts the other.

    Solution: _____

    _____

    _____

    _____

*continued*

d. Obstacle: One lover's pride is injured by the other.

Solution: _____

_____

_____

_____

2.  During the story, both Cupid and Psyche make comments about
what love feels like or means to them.

a. What is your definition of love? _____

_____

_____

_____

_____

b. Do people who are in love act differently than other people?

Explain. _____

_____

_____

_____

_____

*continued*

c. Here are some famous sayings about love. You may list others if you wish. Then note whether you think the saying is true or false. Finally, give reasons for your opinion.

| Saying | True or False | Reason(s) |
|--------|---------------|-----------|
| Love is blind. | | |
| Love means never having to say you're sorry. | | |
| Absence makes the heart grow fonder. | | |
| Love conquers all. | | |
| All's fair in love and war. | | |
| Other saying: | | |
| Other saying: | | |

Name _____

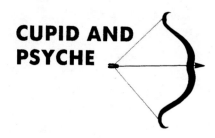

**CUPID AND PSYCHE**

## IT HAPPENED LIKE THIS

Write the letter of the best answer on the line.

_____ 1. Venus plots against Psyche because
   a. she is jealous of Psyche's beauty.
   b. Psyche has mocked Venus.
   c. Jupiter wants to teach Psyche a lesson.

_____ 2. Cupid is so stunned by Psyche's beauty that he
   a. tries to capture her.
   b. shoots himself with an arrow.
   c. wants to become human.

_____ 3. Venus casts a spell on Psyche and makes Psyche
   a. unwanted and unloved.
   b. forgetful and careless.
   c. proud and vain.

_____ 4. When Cupid abandons Venus, there is
   a. joy on Mount Olympus.
   b. an outbreak of disease around Greece.
   c. no more romance in the world.

_____ 5. According to the oracle of Apollo, Psyche will
   a. never marry.
   b. not marry a mortal man.
   c. be sacrificed to the gods.

_____ 6. Cupid remains invisible to Psyche because
   a. she is human and is not allowed to see a god.
   b. Venus has put a spell on Psyche's eyes.
   c. he doesn't want her to love him for his looks.

_____ 7. Psyche's sisters suggest her husband is a monster because he
   a. refuses to let Psyche see him.
   b. won't let Psyche visit them at their palaces.
   c. doesn't have lunch with them.

_____ 8. Because her fear is greater than her love, Psyche
   a. goes home with her sisters.
   b. lights a candle to look at Cupid.
   c. refuses to sleep with Cupid until she sees him.

_____ 9. Psyche completes each of Venus' tasks because
   a. Jupiter won't let her fail.
   b. Cupid sends her help.
   c. Psyche's anger and pride give her strength.

_____ 10. Psyche drinks the cup of nectar and becomes
   a. immortal.
   b. more lovely than ever.
   c. smarter than Cupid.

RETOLD CLASSIC MYTHS, VOL. 1

Name _____

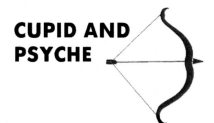

## VOCABULARY REVIEW

These sentences are taken from the story. Circle the
answer that comes closest in meaning to each word in
**dark type**.

1. "Every day, men would **throng** the hallways of the palace just to
   catch a glimpse of lovely Psyche."
   
   a. visit          b. mob          c. stroll

2. "The goddess finally found out why she was being neglected. All
   the mortals were paying **homage** to Psyche instead!"
   
   a. praise          b. sacrifices          c. taxes

3. "Looking at the **somber** faces around her, she said, . . .'Go now. I
   want to meet my fate alone.' "
   
   a. gloomy          b. lonely          c. tense

4. "Psyche felt her life was almost perfect. Just one thing bothered
   her. So one night she **broached** her concern."
   
   a. questioned          b. faced          c. presented

5. "More and more she thought about her family. . . . Had they
   stopped **mourning** for her?"
   
   a. grieving          b. hating          c. loving

6. " 'My servants . . . are always at hand and yet never underfoot.
   They also are very talented musicians. Would you like music with
   your meal?' With **bemused** looks, the sisters nodded."
   
   a. relaxed          b. confused          c. happy

7. "As the flame **wavered** in her shaking hand, Psyche tiptoed back to
   the bed."
   
   a. died          b. swelled          c. flickered

8. " . . . the little creatures moved over the pile of seeds. With quick
   **efficiency**, they sorted the grain."
   
   a. energy          b. skillfulness          c. motions

9. "Exhaustion poured over her. Almost instantly she fell into a
   **stupor**."
   
   a. pit          b. trance          c. disagreement

10. "After the young wife was bathed and freshly dressed, she was
    **ushered** to Jupiter's throne."
    
    a. guided          b. carried          c. rushed

113

**CUPID AND
PSYCHE**

## LITERARY FOCUS: ALLEGORY

"Cupid and Psyche" can be read as more than just a love story. It is also an *allegory*.

Allegories are stories that work on two levels. On the first level—the *literal level*—the allegory tells a story of adventure or romance. On the second level—the *figurative level*—an allegory teaches a moral or truth about human nature by using symbols. These symbols may be found in characters, events, or settings.

For instance, in John Bunyan's *Pilgrim's Progress,* the main character is called Christian. On the literal level, he is a character who journeys to a distant place called Heavenly City. On the figurative level, he stands for all Christians who journey through life trying to reach Heaven.

Now decide how "Cupid and Psyche" can be read allegorically. On the chart below, suggest an allegorical meaning for each literal element. Then give evidence to support your view.

| Literal Level | Figurative Meaning | Evidence |
|---|---|---|
| 1.  Cupid | | |
| 2.  Psyche | | |
| 3.  Oracle | | |
| 4.  Mountains | | |

*continued*

| Literal Level | Figurative Meaning | Evidence |
|---|---|---|
| 5. Cupid's palace | | |
| 6. Venus' tasks | | |
| 7. Proserpina's box | | |
| 8. Cupid and Psyche's marriage on Olympus | | |

Name _____

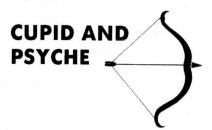

## THE READING-WRITING CONNECTION: UNLOCKING PASSAGES

Answer the questions about these quotes taken from "Cupid and Psyche." (Go back to the story if you need more clues.) Write your response to part *c* of each question on a separate sheet of paper.

1. "At once Cupid felt the sweet poison spread through his veins. He felt his heart swell with passion. Then he grew numb and dizzy with great joy. So this must be what love felt like!" (page 107)

   a. What does the passage mean as used in the story?

   _____

   _____

   b. What must Cupid's life have been like before he felt love?

   _____

   _____

   _____

   c. **Journal writing:** Write about a time in your life when you or someone you know felt this same feeling of love. Was it like being shot by an arrow? Why or why not?

2. " 'I would rather have your respect than ten thousand compliments about my face,' Psyche admitted.

   [Cupid said,] 'Well, you understand then. I also do not wish to be judged by my appearance. No, judge me by my actions and your own heart.' " (page 115)

   a. What does the passage mean as used in the story?

   _____

   _____

*continued*

b. Cupid wishes to be judged by his actions. What kind of person does this statement suggest he is?

_____

_____

_____

_____

c. **Journal writing:** Write about a time when you made the mistake of judging someone by appearances. What kind of person did he or she appear to be? How did his or her actions show you a different person?

3.   " 'Your heart was beautiful. But it has grown ugly from fear and doubt. And love cannot live where the heart does not trust.' " (page 121)

a. What does the passage mean as used in the story?

_____

_____

b. Why does Psyche let her fears take over? What might have happened if Psyche had continued to trust with her heart?

_____

_____

_____

_____

c. **Journal writing:** Write about a time when you failed to trust a friend or a friend lost trust in you. What happened to the relationship?

**CUPID AND PSYCHE**

## WRITING CORNER: SENDING A MESSAGE

The tale of Cupid and Psyche can be read as an allegory. You might recall that an allegory is a story with a message where characters and settings stand for some trait or idea.

Now try writing your own allegory. Begin by deciding what message you want to communicate. The example below may give you an idea.

---

**Message**

      True wisdom is a combination of book learning and common sense.

---

Next create characters to help communicate your message. Using the message above, you could invent the following characters.

---

**Characters**

| Name | Stands for |
|------|-----------|
| Professor Bookman | Book learning |
| Frank Wise | Common sense |
| Hope Lerner | Desire to learn |

---

Setting can also be allegorical. Look at the following examples.

---

**Settings**

| Name | Stands for |
|------|-----------|
| Dark Valley | Ignorance |
| City of Light | Wisdom, true knowledge |
| Ivory Towers | Book learning |
| Richfield | Common sense |
| Crossroad | Combination of book learning and common sense |

---

Once you have message, characters, and setting in mind, create your plot. Remember that your goal is to communicate your message.

*continued*

---

**Plot Outline**

   Hope Lerner receives a partially coded message. The part that she can read tells her to seek the City of Light. But no one in Dark Valley, where Hope lives, knows where the city is.

   Hope sets out on a quest for the city. On the way, she stops at Ivory Towers. There she finds Professor Bookman. Bookman can read part of her message but not all.

   Hope continues her journey. At Richfield, she stops again and meets Frank Wise. Frank decodes the rest of the message, which Hope sees is telling her where the City of Light lies: at the crossroad between Ivory Towers and Richfield. Hope finds the city and joyfully enters it.

---

With these examples in mind, outline your own allegory.

---

**Outline of Your Allegory**

**Message** _____

_____

_____

**Characters**

   **Name**                          **Stands for**




**Settings**

   **Name**                          **Stands for**

---

*continued*

**Plot Outline**

_____

_____

_____

_____

_____

_____

_____

_____

_____

_____

_____

_____

_____

_____

After you complete your outline, you may wish to write out your allegory in more complete form on your own paper. Of course, it is important to communicate your message. But feel free to dress up your allegory with lively conversation and colorful descriptions.

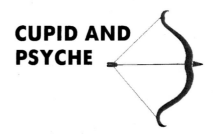

## ONE STEP FURTHER

### Class discussion

1. Are most of the characters in this story all good or all evil? Or are they both good and evil? Give evidence for your views.

2. How do jealousy and suspicion help unite Cupid and Psyche? How do these emotions tear them apart?

3. Why is it ironic that Cupid shoots himself in the foot with a love arrow? Why might this turn of events make him the laughingstock of Olympus?

4. Psyche insists on meeting her fate alone on the mountaintop. What does this reveal about her character? What else does she do, say, or think in the story to show this same character trait?

5. Psyche protests that beauty is not important to her. Do you think she is being honest? Does she get into trouble because she values appearances or because she is merely curious? Explain.

6. How do Cupid's stubbornness and pride affect his love for Psyche? Does anyone else in the story share those same flaws? Give examples to support your opinion.

7. Why does Jupiter allow Psyche to become immortal? Do you think his decision is a good one? Why or why not?

8. Do you think Cupid and Psyche are likely to live happily ever after? Why or why not?

### Written or oral reports

1. Read about Cupid in other myths such as "Jason and the Golden Fleece" or "The Theft of Persephone." Write a short report summarizing Cupid's role.

2. Find out more about Venus. Compare the way her character is sketched in this story to the way that she is portrayed in other myths.

3. First, find a definition of the literary term *allusion*. Then locate a copy of either John Keats' "Ode to Psyche" or Robert Bridge's "Eros and Psyche." Read the poem and explain to your class how allusions are used.

### Creative writing activities

1. As a symbol of love, Cupid is linked to Valentine's Day. Write what he and Psyche would say to each other if they traded valentines. Your messages might be in the form of letters or poems.

2. Cupid quarrels with Venus and refuses to do his job, so the world becomes a "desert of emotion." Write a news release that details the state of the world as a result. (You might find photographs that could accompany your story.)

3. Suppose the story didn't end the way that it did. Write a different ending. Go back to Cupid's rejection of Psyche and tell your version of the story from there.

### Artistic activities

1. Cupid has not always been illustrated as a chubby infant with wings and a bow and arrow. Find other pictures of him and make a collage using these different images.

2. Design the set and costumes for one or two scenes of a stage production of *Cupid and Psyche*.

3. Find—or write—songs to capture the mood of various scenes in the myth. You may wish to write your own lyrics to accompany the tunes.

*continued*

## Small-group activities

1. Select one or more of Cupid's comments about the heart and love. (For example, " 'Aren't the emotions you feel better than what you might see, dear wife?' ") Debate the pros and cons of the statement(s).

2. Suppose Psyche's sisters, her parents, and one or more of her suitors had been at Psyche's wedding. With your group members, stage and enact the wedding feast scene on Olympus and include these characters just mentioned. Also, assign roles for the following characters: Cupid, Psyche, Venus, and Jupiter. Carefully consider what each person would be likely to say to the bride and groom. You might even want to think of appropriate gifts to the newly married couple.

## JASON AND THE GOLDEN FLEECE

# PREREADING ACTIVITIES

### Story Themes

Several themes of "Jason and the Golden Fleece" are listed below. They will help you prepare activities which will stimulate students' interest and involvement in the story.

1.) People seek adventure for many reasons.
2.) For some, the thrill of danger is enough motivation to face great odds.
3.) Forces beyond your control can influence your life.
4.) A broken promise can have tragic results.
5.) Evil is sometimes done in the name of love.

### Spotlight on Vocabulary
### [Guided Practice]

*Objective:*

The learner will demonstrate an understanding of ten vocabulary words by showing which word belongs in each of ten sentences.

*Skill level:*

Knowledge/recall; application

*Description:*

This exercise introduces students to ten words in the story which may be new to them. First students preview the words and their definitions. Then they use the words to complete ten sentences.

The sentences discuss topics familiar to most students, so they can see how the new words fit into their existing web of knowledge. The goal of the exercise is to help students read the story more easily. Complete mastery of the vocabulary words at this stage is not expected.

*Suggestion:*

If prereading vocabulary work is kept short, word study can build interest without dampening enthusiasm. Exposure

to these ten selected words will give students a head start toward understanding the story. A *postreading* vocabulary check and suggestions for further vocabulary study are provided for use *after* students have read the story.

### Setting the Stage
### [Anticipatory Set]

*Objective:*

The learner will gain an understanding of what leads people to seek adventure by answering questions about an adventure he or she has had. The learner will also show an understanding of the forces in his or her life by evaluating an experience when he or she was controlled by another person.

*Skill level:*

Application; analysis

*Description:*

First students are asked to describe an adventure of their own and the risk involved in that adventure. Then they are to write the ingredients for their own great adventure. Next students answer questions about a time when they did not feel in control of a situation. They identify what forces were in control and analyze how they felt about this. Finally students decide if they would want to have total control or some guidance in their own lives.

*Suggestion:*

Students may wish to discuss which movie or book adventures they would most like to experience themselves. Have them also discuss the risks involved. When discussing fate, try offering students various quotes to help them decide how they view the influence of fate in their own lives.

# JASON AND THE GOLDEN FLEECE

## POSTREADING ACTIVITIES

### It Happened Like This
### [Check for Understanding]

*Objective:*

The learner will demonstrate comprehension of the story by correctly answering ten multiple-choice questions.

*Skill level:*

Knowledge; comprehension

*Description:*

This exercise tests recall of important facts in the story. Students identify, from three choices, the answer that correctly completes each of ten sentences.

*Suggestion:*

Page number references on the response key show where the answer to each question can be found. These page numbers can be given to students who are taking an open-book test. The page numbers are also helpful when discussing the quiz after papers have been corrected.

### Vocabulary Review
### [Check for Understanding]

*Objective:*

The learner will demonstrate an understanding of ten words by identifying the correct synonym for each.

*Skill level:*

Knowledge

*Description:*

This exercise tests mastery of the ten words introduced in the **Spotlight on Vocabulary** exercise. The words are presented in the context of sentences taken directly from the story. Students identify, from three choices, the correct synonym for each word.

*Suggestion:*

Results of the vocabulary check will show which words students find most difficult. You may wish to provide further reinforcement for problem words.

### Literary Focus: Character Motivation
### [Guided or Independent Practice]

*Objective:*

The learner will complete a chart and draw conclusions to demonstrate an understanding of the relationship between motivation and character action.

*Skill level:*

Analysis; evaluation

*Description:*

Students are given a list of ten actions carried out by characters in the story. They are asked to complete a chart listing a character's motivation for that action and the result of the action. Then they use the chart to answer questions about specific characters and what their motivation reveals about them. They also evaluate and consider the results of both good and bad motivation.

*Suggestion:*

Before completing the chart, students may find it helpful to discuss their own motivation for doing something. Help them to realize that what may motivate one person may have no influence on someone else.

### The Reading-Writing Connection:
### Unlocking Passages
### [Guided or Independent Practice]

*Objective:*

The learner will demonstrate an ability to make inferences by answering questions based on quotations from the story.

*Skill level:*

Comprehension; application; analysis

*Description:*

First students read a quotation; then they answer three questions about the quote.

*continued*

# JASON AND THE GOLDEN FLEECE

The first question requires an interpretation of the quote. The second question requires an inference. The third question, to be answered in a journal entry, asks students to relate the quotation to their personal experience.

The questions are intended to lead students to greater understanding and appreciation of the story. The questions also allow students to bridge the gap between their own knowledge and story concepts.

Quotation 1 concerns the benefits of being in Hera's favor. Quotation 2 concerns Medea's fated love for Jason. Quotation 3 concerns Jason's horror at what Medea will do in the name of love.

*Suggestion:*

Make the questions the subject of small-group or class discussion.

## Writing Corner: Conducting an Interview [Extending Students' Thinking]

*Objective:*

The learner will demonstrate an understanding of how to conduct an interview by designing thoughtful interview questions and using them in an interview situation.

*Skill level:*

Analysis; synthesis; evaluation

*Description:*

First students are asked to choose a character from the myth to interview for a fictional magazine. Then they are to write five in-depth interview questions for that character. At the conclusion of this activity, students will role-play, taking turns being an interviewer and a character being interviewed.

*Suggestion:*

Students may enjoy using a tape recorder or video camera to record the interviews.

## One Step Further [Extending Students' Thinking]

*Objective:*

The learner will demonstrate an ability to interpret, compare, contrast, and/or create by participating in discussions, preparing reports, or completing special projects.

*Skill level:*

Application; analysis; synthesis; evaluation

*Description:*

Students choose from an array of suggested follow-up activities which will help them process the story and respond creatively to the story's conflicts and themes. The activities encourage students of varying abilities to employ higher-level thinking skills.

*Suggestion:*

You may wish to use this page as a teacher reference and assign projects to individuals or groups. However the page may also be reproduced so that students can select their own topics.

Although the suggested activities are divided into categories such as **Class discussion** and **Written or oral reports**, most of the topics can be adapted for use in many ways.

# JASON AND THE GOLDEN FLEECE

## SPOTLIGHT ON VOCABULARY

Study the words and meanings shown in the box.
Then complete each sentence below by writing the
correct word on the line.

| | |
|---|---|
| **craved**—desired; longed for | **rapt**—paying complete attention; absorbed |
| **invincible**—unable to be overcome; unconquerable | **refrain**—withhold; stop |
| **peril**—great risk or danger | **rekindled**—lighted again |
| **predicament**—a difficult or troubling situation | **threshold**—doorway; entrance |
| | **vanity**—too much pride in oneself |
| | **vitality**—energy |

1. A dog stood guard at the _____ of the front door.

2. People noticed Giorgio's _____ because he was always stopping in front of mirrors to admire his looks.

3. Fran was in (a an) _____ after she booked two babysitting jobs for the same time.

4. The audience stared with _____ attention, while the trainer put her arm in the lion's open mouth.

5. Cory hadn't eaten chocolate in weeks, but he still _____ it every day.

6. The flood put the campers in _____ of drowning.

7. The campfire had to be _____ every time the falling snow put it out.

8. After a winning basketball season, we thought we were _____ and that no team could beat us.

9. The enthusiasm and _____ of youth are often admired by older people.

10. Ms. Tate insisted her students _____ from talking and be silent while taking a test.

Name _____

## SETTING THE STAGE

These exercises will help you get ready to read
"Jason and the Golden Fleece." Prepare to discuss
the questions by jotting down answers on the lines.

1. Jason, the hero of the story, loves adventure. He does not expect glory,
   wealth, or fame from his adventures. He simply seeks the thrill of a tough
   challenge. If Jason could write a recipe for the perfect adventure, danger
   would be a necessary item.
   
   Think about a time when you had an adventure.

   a. Briefly describe your adventure.

   _____

   _____

   _____

   _____

   b. What role did risk or uncertainty play in your adventure?

   _____

   _____

   _____

   c. Suppose you could write a recipe for an adventure. What kinds of people, places, or activities would make a great adventure for you?

   _____

   _____

   _____

   _____

   _____

*continued*

**PREREADING**

2.  Jason's life is highly influenced by gods and goddesses. They often play important but unseen roles in his life.

a. Think about a time in your life when everything was not controlled by you. Describe what happened.

_____

_____

_____

_____

_____

b. Tell who or what was in control. Describe your feelings about not controlling events.

_____

_____

_____

_____

_____

c. If you could choose, would you want to be in charge of your life? Or would you want someone else to control your life? Explain.

_____

_____

_____

_____

_____

Name _____

## IT HAPPENED LIKE THIS

Write the letter of the best answer on the line.

____ 1. Pelias is upset when Jason appears because he fears Jason might
a. demand to marry his daughter.
b. kill him.
c. destroy his kingdom.

____ 2. In return for the Golden Fleece, Pelias promises to
a. tell Jason of its magical power.
b. spare Jason's mother.
c. let Jason have Aeson's throne.

____ 3. On the journey to Colchis, the Argonauts are aided by
a. Argus, who repairs the ship.
b. the Harpies, who chase away sea monsters.
c. Hera, who gives fair winds and good luck.

____ 4. Aeetes gives Jason all these tasks *except:*
a. slaying the monster who destroys Aeetes' crops.
b. plowing a field with fire-breathing bulls.
c. fighting warriors who grow from a dragon's teeth.

____ 5. To help Jason with the tasks, Medea
a. gives him advice and an ointment.
b. prays to Hera.
c. arms him with a magic shield.

____ 6. Medea murders Apsyrtus and chops up his body because she knows her
a. sacrifice will please the gods.
b. brother wanted to kill Jason.
c. father will stop to gather his son's body.

____ 7. Instead of restoring Pelias' youth, Medea
a. gives Pelias' remaining years to Aeson.
b. tricks his daughters into murdering him.
c. makes Pelias age more quickly.

____ 8. Jason and Medea flee to Corinth where they live happily until
a. Jason decides to marry Creusa.
b. Creon orders them to leave.
c. Medea falls in love with Creon.

____ 9. Seeking revenge, Medea
a. makes Jason blind and lame.
b. kills Creon and exiles Creusa.
c. kills Creusa and her own two sons.

____ 10. Jason spends his last days
a. praying to the gods for help.
b. wandering lonely and friendless.
c. trying to find Medea.

# JASON AND THE GOLDEN FLEECE

## VOCABULARY REVIEW

These sentences are taken from the story. Circle the
answer that comes closest in meaning to each word in
**dark type**.

1. "He knew the quest would be filled with **peril**."
   a. pain          b. danger          c. loss

2. " 'You've done your work already,' said the goddess. 'Now kindly
   **refrain** from killing Zeus' precious hounds.' "
   a. retreat        b. stop            c. walk away

3. "A mist, sent by Hera, hid them as they marched. It lifted to reveal
   them only when they were safely at the palace **threshold**."
   a. window         b. cellar          c. entrance

4. "All that night they discussed Jason's **predicament**."
   a. trouble        b. argument        c. decision

5. "She was completely overwhelmed with love. She stared at him,
   **rapt** and silent."
   a. amused         b. surprised       c. absorbed

6. " 'Rub this on your sword,' she said. 'For one day only, it will
   make you **invincible**.' "
   a. invisible      b. unconquerable   c. bold

7. "Jason's fear was **rekindled** for a moment."
   a. controlled     b. remembered      c. lighted
      again                                again

8. " 'Poor, unsleeping creature,' she cooed. 'How long have you
   **craved** a little taste of sleep?' "
   a. desired        b. stolen          c. hidden

9. "Soon Aeson stirred from his magic sleep. He sat up, astonished at
   his new **vitality**."
   a. energy         b. position        c. understanding

10. " 'I'll give her a gift—one that suits her **vanity**.' "
    a. pride         b. ambition        c. price

RETOLD CLASSIC MYTHS, VOL. 1
Copyright 1990. Perfection Learning Corporation, Logan, Iowa 51546

**JASON AND THE GOLDEN FLEECE**

## LITERARY FOCUS: CHARACTER MOTIVATION

One way to understand a character is to consider the character's *motivation* or reasons for doing something. Below is a chart that supplies you with characters' actions. For each action, list the character's motivation and the results of that action. An example is given.

| Character's Action | Motivation | Result of Action |
|---|---|---|
| *Example:* Aeson decides to retire. | Aeson is tired of ruling. | Pelias takes over the kingdom. |
| 1. Pelias tempts Jason to go in search of the Golden Fleece. | | |
| 2. Jason accepts Pelias' request. | | |
| 3. Hera aids the Argonauts. | | |
| 4. Phineus tells the Argonauts how to get through the Symplegades. | | |
| 5. Eros casts a spell on Medea. | | |

*continued*

| Character's Action | Motivation | Result of Action |
|---|---|---|
| 6. Aeetes gives Jason two very risky tasks. | | |
| 7. Medea tells Jason how to perform the tasks and gives him a magic ointment. | | |
| 8. Medea chops up Apsyrtus. | | |
| 9. Jason considers marrying Creusa. | | |
| 10. Medea plans to kill her two sons. | | |

*continued*

RETOLD CLASSIC MYTHS, VOL. 1

## Conclusions

1. A character's motivation suggests something about his or her personality. Motivation may show whether a character is clever or foolish, wise or ignorant, adventurous or lazy.

   Select one character from the chart. What motivates the character? What does this suggest about the character? What other examples in the story support your conclusion about the character's personality?

   _____

   _____

   _____

   _____

   _____

   _____

2. Using the chart, decide which are good motivations and which are bad. Now look at the results. Does a good motivation always produce a good result? Does a bad motivation always produce a bad result? Why do you think this is so?

   _____

   _____

   _____

   _____

   _____

   _____

*continued*

3. Review Medea's motivations. In what ways is she self-motivated? In what ways is she controlled or directed by other powers? If Medea were entirely self-motivated, how might the myth have changed?

_____

_____

_____

_____

_____

_____

**JASON AND THE GOLDEN FLEECE**

## THE READING-WRITING CONNECTION: UNLOCKING PASSAGES

Answer the questions about these quotes taken from
"Jason and the Golden Fleece." (Go back to the
story if you need more clues.) Write your response to
part *c* of each question on a separate sheet of paper.

1. "Hera was willful and short-tempered, so it was better to have her
   on your side than against you." (page 134)

   a. What does the passage mean as used in the story?

   _____

   _____

   b. Find examples of Hera getting involved in Jason's adventures.
   How might Jason's adventures have been different if Hera had not
   favored him and helped him?

   _____

   _____

   _____

   _____

   c. **Journal writing:** Describe a time when it was better to have someone on your side rather than against you.

2. "But the minute she set eyes on Jason, Eros shot his arrow of love.
   He aimed well, and Medea's sad fate was sealed." (page 137)

   a. What does the passage mean as used in the story?

   _____

   _____

*continued*

b. Explain why Medea's fate is described as being "sad."

_____

_____

_____

_____

c. **Journal writing:** Write about a time when Eros' arrow of love struck you or someone you know. Was the outcome sad or happy? Why?

3. "Jason watched Medea's deed with awe and terror. 'What horrors might this woman do out of love for me?' " (page 144)

a. What does the passage mean as used in the story?

_____

_____

b. Explain how Medea's love becomes something that Jason will regret forever.

_____

_____

_____

_____

c. **Journal writing:** When they are in love, people sometimes act unwisely, strangely, or even foolishly. Describe a time when you or someone you know did something out of the ordinary because of love.

# JASON AND THE GOLDEN FLEECE

## WRITING CORNER: CONDUCTING AN INTERVIEW

Imagine that you have been given the opportunity to meet characters from "Jason and the Golden Fleece." As a magazine reporter, you decide to write an interview of one of the characters.

---

1. **The Character:** It may seem obvious that you should interview Jason or Medea. However, there are other strong possibilities. For example, Aeson, Aeetes, Eros, or Hera might also be good choices.

   Write the name of the character you would like to interview: _____

2. **The Interview Questions:** Before you begin the interview, decide what kind of information you want. Some areas you may want to explore include the following:

   - background
   - special interests and skills
   - successes
   - opinions

   Keep these areas in mind as you write your interview questions. Avoid questions which can simply be answered yes or no. You won't get much information from such questions. Two sample questions have been provided.

   A question for Jason: *What are your thoughts about Medea's murder of her brother?*

   or

   A question for Medea: *What was your life like before you met Jason?*

*continued*

Name ______________________

# JASON AND THE GOLDEN FLEECE

Now it's your turn. Write five interview questions for your character.

a. ______________________

______________________

______________________

b. ______________________

______________________

______________________

c. ______________________

______________________

______________________

d. ______________________

______________________

______________________

e. ______________________

______________________

______________________

*continued*

3.  **The Interview:** Pair up with a classmate who plans to interview a
    different character than the one you picked. With your classmate
    playing the part of your character, ask the questions you prepared.
    Either take notes or tape the character's answers. Feel free to ask
    more questions than the ones you prepared.

    After the first interview, switch roles. Now you will pretend to
    be a character from the myth and answer your classmate's questions.
    As you play the character, use story facts and your imagination to
    answer interview questions.

## ONE STEP FURTHER

### Class discussion

1. The story of Jason's quest for the Golden Fleece has been popular for years. Why do you think this myth has been so popular? What is it about the story that continues to attract readers?

2. Jason is not the only character in the story who enjoys adventure. What other characters like a good adventure? What makes Jason different from these other characters?

3. Along with their supernatural powers, Greek gods and goddesses also possess human feelings and traits. In the story, how do the gods and goddesses use their powers? In what ways do they act like humans or display human traits? Why do you think the ancient Greeks viewed their gods and goddesses with human and supernatural traits?

4. Medea is a sorceress. At times she uses her magic for good purposes. At other times, she uses it for bad or evil reasons. Give some examples of Medea's magic used for good reasons. Then give examples where it is used for bad reasons. Why do you think she uses her magic for both good and bad purposes?

5. Many characters lose their lives because of Medea's love for Jason. Are these deaths necessary or unnecessary? Explain your response. What conclusions can you make about the force that controls Medea? Does it cause her to murder or are the murders her own idea?

6. Why would Jason have preferred to die while facing danger? Was it fitting or unfair for Jason to die alone and unloved? Give reasons for your opinion.

### Written or oral reports

1. Homer's *Odyssey* tells the story of Odysseus, another Greek hero who experiences many adventures. Read about one of Odysseus' adventures. Then prepare a report on how Odysseus' adventure is similar to or different from Jason's. One adventure you might enjoy is the story of Circe and Odysseus. You might also like to read about Odysseus' adventure with the Cyclops. (Ask your teacher for other suggestions.)

2. Study another pair of lovers in Greek myth whose relationship ended unhappily, and compare them to Jason and Medea. In your report, compare the lovers' backgrounds and traits and the reasons the relationships fell apart. Finally, conclude which love story is most tragic and explain your view. Some lovers from Greek myths are suggested below.
   a. Aeneas and Dido
   b. Agamemnon and Clytemnestra
   c. Heracles and Deianira
   d. Narcissus and Echo
   e. Glaucus and Scylla

3. "Jason and the Golden Fleece" is not the only story in which Medea appears. Set out on a quest for Medea. Go to your library and see what other poems, plays, stories, or operas use Medea as a character. How is Medea portrayed in these other selections? Make a list of your findings, and share the information with your classmates.

### Creative writing activities

1. Suppose Jason kept a diary while he was on his quest for the Golden Fleece. Select a couple of the adventures and record them as Jason would have recalled them in his diary.

*continued*

2. The story says that Medea thought longingly of her father and home. Although she knows that she cannot return, it is possible that she could have written her father a letter. Write Medea's letter as you think she may have written it. Include events from the story and create some new ones.

3. Imagine that you are a newspaper reporter for the *Greek National Press*. You are the only reporter permitted to travel with the Argonauts. Your assignment is to prepare daily press releases for the paper, highlighting the main events of each day. Select one day and write the story that you would send back to your editor.

### Artistic activities

1. A scene from "Jason and the Golden Fleece" is to be the cover illustration for a new book, *Tales from Mythology*. Create the illustration that will be featured on the cover. Design your picture to attract readers and make them want to pick up the book.

2. Using modeling clay or pottery clay, design a bust or statue of Jason or some other character. Or you may design a piece of pottery and paint a scene from the myth on it.

3. Illustrate a scene from the story that has a mythological creature. For example, you may choose to draw Zeus' Harpies attacking Phineus. Other possibilities might be the dragon protecting the Golden Fleece or a picture of Talus rising out of the sea.

### Small-group discussion

1. Choose sides and debate this question: Is Medea a victim of love who could not control her actions or is she a cold-blooded killer? After each small group debates the issue, you may want to divide the class into three sections and hold a mock trial for Medea's crimes. One group would act as the defense, one group would prepare and present the prosecution's evidence, and the third group would act as the jury.

2. Draw a map of the ancient world, including Greece. Then trace Jason's journey as he searched for the Golden Fleece. Using a symbol or small picture, mark each stop or place where the *Argo's* crew met with trouble. (You will need to find sources in the library to help you with this one.) Divide up the tasks among group members.

# RESPONSE KEY

## CREATION OF THE TITANS AND GODS

### Spotlight on Vocabulary
1. reign; 2. inevitable; 3. thwarted; 4. vial; 5. sprouted; 6. immortal;
7. sickle; 8. infinite; 9. counsel; 10. agile.

### It Happened Like This
1. a (p. 4); 2. b (p. 4); 3. b (p. 5); 4. c (p. 5); 5. a (p. 7); 6. a (p. 7);
7. c (p. 7); 8. b (pp. 9-10); 9. c (p. 10); 10. a (p. 11).

### Vocabulary Review
1. b; 2. a; 3. c; 4. c; 5. b; 6. a; 7. b; 8. a; 9. a; 10. c.

### Literary Focus: The Clash of the Titans
1. Uranus vs. his offspring, d; 2. Gaea vs. Uranus, d; 3. Cronus vs. his
siblings, d; 4. Cronus vs. fate, e; 5. Cronus vs. self, a, *or* Cronus vs.
fate, e, *or* Cronus vs. Gaea, d; 6. Cronus vs. fate, e; 7. Zeus vs. Cronus,
d; 8. Titans vs. the forces of nature, b *or* Zeus and the Hundred-handed
Ones vs. Cronus and the Titans, d.

## PROMETHEUS

### Spotlight on Vocabulary
1. stern; 2. deceptive; 3. destined; 4. tactic; 5. defied; 6. hovered;
7. provocation; 8. humility; 9. soothed; 10. tend.

### It Happened Like This
1. c (pp. 17-18); 2. a (pp. 18-19); 3. c (p. 19); 4. b (pp. 19-20); 5. b
(p. 21); 6. c (p. 22); 7. a (p. 23); 8. b (p. 24); 9. a (p. 24); 10. c (p. 25).

### Vocabulary Review
1. b; 2. a; 3. a; 4. c; 5. a; 6. b; 7. b; 8. c; 9. b; 10. a.

### Literary Focus: It's Alive!
1. envy and greed, being born *or* becoming living creatures; 2. coal,
ability to sleep; 3. fire *or* flames, growth; 4. fire *or* flames, speech and
hunger; 5. fire, the process of dying *or* hunger; 6. fire, hunger *or* ability
to eat; 7. secret, ability to be free.

## THE TWELVE LABORS OF HERACLES

### Spotlight on Vocabulary
1. gaped; 2. agitated; 3. mulled; 4. intruder; 5. wary; 6. stature; 7. foul;
8. distract; 9. quivered; 10. penance.

### It Happened Like This
1. b (p. 32); 2. a (p. 33); 3. b (p. 35); 4. a (p. 38); 5. b (p. 40); 6. c
(p. 41); 7. b (p. 44); 8. c (p. 49); 9. a (p. 50); 10. c (p. 52).

### Vocabulary Review
1. b; 2. a; 3. a; 4. c; 5. b; 6. a; 7. b; 8. c; 9. a; 10. b.

## CIRCE AND ODYSSEUS

**Spotlight on Vocabulary**

1. poised; 2. elapsed; 3. dense; 4. impish; 5. recoiled; 6. sty; 7. sullen;
8. cower; 9. hazardous; 10. conferred.

**It Happened Like This**

1. b (p. 57); 2. a (p. 58); 3. a (p. 59); 4. b (p. 61); 5. a (p. 62);
6. c (p. 63); 7. c (p. 63); 8. b (p. 64); 9. c (p. 65); 10. a (p. 67).

**Vocabulary Review**

1. c; 2. a; 3. a; 4. b; 5. c; 6. b; 7. b; 8. a; 9. c; 10. b.

## AENEAS' TRIP TO THE UNDERWORLD

**Spotlight on Vocabulary**

1. endured; 2. selflessness; 3. predict; 4. destiny; 5. fork; 6. desperately;
7. assured; 8. collapsed; 9. condemned; 10. descendants.

**It Happened Like This**

1. b (p. 74); 2. c (p. 74); 3. a (pp. 75-76); 4. a (p. 77); 5. a (p. 79);
6. c (p. 80); 7. a (p. 81); 8. b (pp. 82-83); 9. b (p. 83); 10. a (pp. 83-84).

**Vocabulary Review**

1. b; 2. c; 3. a; 4. a; 5. b; 6. b; 7. a; 8. c; 9. b; 10. c.

**Literary Focus: Plot Devices**

1. device: Aeneas' vision, plot advance: Aeneas and the Trojans flee
Troy; 2. device: Anchises' ghost; 3. plot advance: Aeneas finds the Sibyl;
4. device: two doves; 5. plot advance: Aeneas and the Sibyl are allowed
into the Underworld; 6. plot advance: Charon ferries Aeneas across the
river; 7. device: drugged cake; 8. device: golden bough; 9. plot advance:
Aeneas and the Trojans set off to find their promised home.

## THE FOLLIES OF MIDAS

**Spotlight on Vocabulary**

1. procession; 2. tutor; 3. confiding; 4. renounce; 5. verdict;
6. deliriously; 7. enraptured; 8. inadequate; 9. nudged; 10. gracious.

**It Happened Like This**

1. b (p. 92); 2. c (p. 93); 3. a (p. 94); 4. a (p. 96); 5. b (p. 96);
6. b (p. 97); 7. c (p. 98); 8. a (p. 98); 9. a (p. 99); 10. c (p. 99).

**Vocabulary Review**

1. c; 2. b; 3. a; 4. a; 5. b; 6. a; 7. b; 8. c; 9. a; 10. a.

**Literary Focus: Humor**

1. H; 2. S; 3. U; 4. S, U; 5. S; 6. I, H; 7. S; 8. H; 9. U, I.

## CUPID AND PSYCHE

**Spotlight on Vocabulary**

1. throng; 2. wavered; 3. homage; 4. mourning; 5. bemused;
6. broached; 7. ushered; 8. somber; 9. efficiency; 10. stupor.

**It Happened Like This**

1. a (p. 106); 2. b (p. 107); 3. a (p. 108); 4. c (p. 109); 5. b (p. 110);
6. c (p. 115); 7. a (p. 118); 8. b (p. 120); 9. b (p. 124); 10. a (p. 125).

**Vocabulary Review**

1. b; 2. a; 3. a; 4. c; 5. a; 6. b; 7. c; 8. b; 9. b; 10. a.

**Literary Focus: Allegory**

Figurative level: 1. heart, love; 2. soul or mind; 3. wisdom, future, fate;
4. obstacle, danger, unknown, fate, etc. 5. paradise, happiness;
6. obstacle, passage to adulthood; price of love, danger; 7. beauty,
mystery, temptation; 8. union of the heart and soul/mind.

## JASON AND THE GOLDEN FLEECE

**Spotlight on Vocabulary**

1. threshold; 2. vanity; 3. predicament; 4. rapt; 5. craved; 6. peril;
7. rekindled; 8. invincible; 9. vitality; 10. refrain.

**It Happened Like This**

1. b (p. 132); 2. c (p. 132); 3. c (p. 134); 4. a (p. 138); 5. a (pp. 139-40);
6. c (p. 143); 7. b (p. 148); 8. a (p. 148); 9. c (pp. 149-50); 10. b
(p. 150).

**Vocabulary Review**

1. b; 2. b; 3. c; 4. a; 5. c; 6. b; 7. c; 8. a; 9. a; 10. a.

**Literary Focus: Character Motivation**

1. Motivation: Pelias hopes Jason will die on the perilous quest. Result:
Jason believes he will gain the throne. 2. Motivation: Jason is thrilled
with the idea of an adventure. Result: Jason begins the quest. 3. Motivation: Hera is fond of Jason. Result: The Argonauts get "fair winds and
good fortune." 4. Motivation: Phineus is grateful to the Argonauts for
saving him. Result: The Argonauts sail safely through the Symplegades.
5. Motivation: Hera wants Medea to help Jason. Result: Medea falls in
love with Jason. 6. Motivation: Aeetes hopes Jason will be killed. Result:
Jason accepts the challenge but realizes the threat. 7. Motivation: Medea
is hopelessly in love with Jason. Result: Jason completes the tasks.
8. Motivation: Medea hopes to stop Aeetes from pursuing Jason. Result:
The Argonauts escape from Colchis. 9. Motivation: Jason will gain
power and wealth. Result: Jason goes ahead with his plan to marry
Creusa, thereby angering Medea. 10. Motivation: Medea won't let her
sons suffer for her sins. Result: Medea kills her sons, then flees.

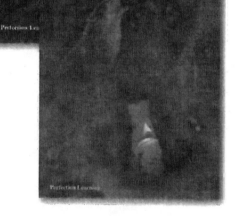